"In this groundbreaking work, John gives survivors (and practitioners) options that work, based on his knowledge and vast experience in the field of trauma and recovery. The tools and strategies that he details are not just life-saving; they are life-enhancing!"

Dr Rosario Margarita A. Aligada,
College of Education Dean, Miriam College,
The Philippines

"This book contains an abundance of concrete ideas, practices and techniques; it's like a trauma re-wiring toolbox in one place: From somatic exercises, such as breathing, to visualizations, useful therapeutic stances (i.e. working with guilt), a basic self-care checklist, working with sleep disturbances, and existential questions of meaning and realizing one's full potential. I would highly recommend it."

Olga Zotova, coach, narrative therapist,
solution focused and EMDR practitioner,
Moscow, Russia

What It Takes to Thrive

to Thrive

Techniques for Severe Trauma and Stress Recovery

John Henden

Principal Trainer and Psychotherapist, John Henden Consultancy Ltd, UK

World Scientific

NEW JERSEY · LONDON · SINGAPORE · BEIJING · SHANGHAI · HONG KONG · TAIPEI · CHENNAI · TOKYO

Published by

World Scientific Publishing Co. Pte. Ltd.
5 Toh Tuck Link, Singapore 596224
USA office: 27 Warren Street, Suite 401-402, Hackensack, NJ 07601
UK office: 57 Shelton Street, Covent Garden, London WC2H 9HE

Library of Congress Cataloging-in-Publication Data
Names: Henden, John, author.
Title: What it takes to thrive : techniques for severe trauma and stress recovery / John Henden,
    John Henden Consultancy, The United Kingdom.
Description: New Jersey : World Scientific, [2017] |
    Includes bibliographical references and index.
Identifiers: LCCN 2017036444| ISBN 9789813229327 (hardcover : alk. paper) |
    ISBN 9789813230217 (pbk. : alk. paper)
Subjects: LCSH: Post-traumatic stress disorder--Treatment. | Psychic trauma--Treatment.
Classification: LCC RC552.P67 H453 2017 | DDC 616.85/21--dc23
LC record available at https://lccn.loc.gov/2017036444

British Library Cataloguing-in-Publication Data
A catalogue record for this book is available from the British Library.

Typeset by Stallion Press
Email: enquire@stallionpress.com

Printed in Singapore

Dedication

I dedicate this book to the many survivors I have known and met, who have shown determination to reach the "thriver" stage in their journey, living life to the full, and, in many cases, gone on to achieve great things. They are shining examples of what is possible (despite the severity of traumatic events they may have experienced either in childhood or in their adult lives) and a great encouragement to others who are, currently, at earlier stages in their journey.

Disclaimer

This book has been written and published for informational purposes and is not intended to serve as a substitute for therapy or treatment of any specific complaint. The author and publisher are providing you, the reader, with information and advice for consideration, but ultimately, each survivor, and spouse/partner/buddy/family member, need to seek out and find whatever works best for them. This book is not intended to be a substitute for professional help when it is needed.

The Book's Purpose

As both a therapist and a trainer, I have worked with severe trauma and stress for nearly 25 years. In that time, I have noted the dire shortage of appropriate skilled help for those in need. Often, where help has been available, it has been the wrong sort of help and/or the practitioner's skills have been insufficient.

Many publications have been designed to provide help for both survivors of severe trauma and stress. Few, however, provide specific tips and techniques for recovery.

The various textbooks aimed at helping practitioners tend to concentrate more on background, awareness, demographics, personality factors and statistics, rather than getting down to specifics on what works. Even those books which do list some tools and techniques, describe just a few, or are overly complicated and technical, appeal to more academic practitioners. This comprehensive guide, with its many tools and techniques, is intended to plug this gap in provision.

This book has been designed to be helpful to both survivors and practitioners alike.

It should be emphasised that most people who experience traumatic life events return to relative normality within a few days or weeks, after talking about it with relatives and friends, or simply processing it, mentally, during this time. It is the 15–20%, having a longer, more pronounced reaction, who can benefit most from this book.

Psychotherapists, counsellors, welfare workers and lay workers who have a heart for working with survivors of severe trauma and stress will find all they need within this book. It is divided into six sections: triggers, flashbacks, intrusive thoughts, sleep disturbance, the "lows", and living life to the full.

Most of the 100+ tools and techniques within are easy to understand and apply, by both survivors of severe trauma and stress and by therapists and counsellors. For welfare workers and lay workers, a basic counselling skills qualification is recommended.

An overriding hope is that the book will encourage even more practitioners to work in the field of severe trauma and stress recovery.

Many avoid working with survivors of severe trauma for the following reasons:

- fear of saying something that will make the person worse,
- fear of hearing something which could have the potential to traumatise,
- the mistaken belief that there are "thousands of experts out there", just waiting for the telephone referral.

All survivors of severe trauma and stress struggle with the issue of lack of control regarding triggers, flashbacks or intrusive thoughts. Learning and applying the techniques within this book will enable them to regain control — not only over their mental and physical experiences but also of their lives.

To ensure the text is as widely accessible as possible, it is intentionally jargon-free.

Another purpose is to give *hope* both to survivors and practitioners. Stories abound from those working in this field, where survivors have been helped not only to manage better after what they have experienced, but also to go on to live fuller lives — and to thrive. This applies equally to victims of armed robbery, near-death experiences, rape, terrorist incidents, adult survivors of child abuse, natural disasters, sudden death and road traffic incidents involving death and carnage.

Although the book's approach is solution-focused, with many of the techniques being either solution-focused or cognitive-behavioural, practitioners of other therapeutic models can incorporate these techniques into their practice.

Introduction

In the following pages are over 100 tools and techniques which have been found to be helpful to tens of thousands of survivors of all types of severe trauma and stress. The emphasis is on simplicity and effectiveness, with a minimum of jargon wherever and whenever possible.

The book's contents are directed at survivors, essentially, as their own personal guide. However, you will see that I am writing to both survivors and practitioners.

If you are a worker/practitioner, counsellor, therapist, psychologist, psychiatrist, medical officer/doctor, welfare worker, helpline worker or experienced lay worker, you will find the contents of this manual an invaluable addition to your "toolbox" when working with all sorts of survivors. Your fellow practitioners have been using and field testing these tools and techniques for years. The evidence base for solution focus is now well established (see Appendix I). Also, the practice-based evidence continues to grow, and, more importantly, the personal testimonies of survivors of death and carnage of one sort or another, or other traumatic events, who have regained control and gone on to live relatively trouble-free and fulfilling lives. As practitioners, in my view, we have both an ethical responsibility and a duty of care to undertake this important work rather than medicating for symptom alleviation and providing "support". The outcomes for survivors when workers avoid getting involved in this work or use inappropriate treatments can be unsatisfactory at best and tragic at worst. Stories of the latter are all too numerous to mention. What follows in the pages ahead will not only give great confidence to workers but also the fullest range of tools and techniques for them to get on with doing an even more effective job. If you need inspiration and encouragement right now, it may be helpful to read Appendices A–G first before continuing to the main sections of the book.

You may like to read through the pages of this book on behalf of a friend or relative who, at the moment, is having a few difficulties of some sort or another. "Buddy-aid" is powerful and you may be surprised how helpful you can be.

You may have survived a recent (or not-so-recent) road traffic incident and are affected still by some thoughts and images or avoidance reactions. This book will give you what you need to lay these thoughts, images and feelings to rest. Although memories of traumatic incidents stay with us (they do fade a little with time), the main objectives of trauma recovery work are *to be affected by them no longer.* I will never forget all the awful things I experienced both as a child and as an adult, but I can live a full and productive life, regardless.

It maybe you saw someone who died or was killed or maimed before your very eyes. You may have experienced much death and carnage. If so, you too may find this book helpful. If you are a survivor of a near-death ("near-miss") experience, where you think frequently about what might have occurred, this book is for you too. Whatever trauma you might have experienced, there is something here for you.

For some survivors, it will take courage and resolve to pick up this book and thumb through its pages to see what may be helpful or useful for either yourself or others. It does not mean you have "gone soft", are "weak", or in some way are a lesser person than you are. Indeed, often quite the opposite is the case. By following some or many of the suggestions made, in the sections that follow, you will become even stronger and more resilient than you are already. You too can look forward to living a fuller and more satisfying life. A spin-off could be that you will be in a better position to help others who may have the need too. Where a sense of guilt, fear, shame and anxiety may have been present, you can replace this/these with a sense of renewed direction and purpose in life.

You will notice that the text within this book is more than single-spaced and of a larger point size than usual.

This is to make it even more user-friendly and accessible than it is already.

When trying out various tools and techniques within the six sections of this book, if one or other does not work for you (or your client), it is not about "failure". It means simply that the tool or technique does not suit at this point in time and that you may need to try another. This fits well with a basic principle of the solution-focused approach: "going with what works".

How to Use This Book

You will find that the tools and techniques within the book are laid out under the following six sections:

1. Triggers
2. Flashbacks
3. Unwelcome thoughts
4. Dealing with the lows
5. Disturbed sleep
6. Living life to the full: meaning and purpose in life

For quick results, go to the section that most applies. Within each section, often the term "horses for courses"

applies. Some survivors find one tool or technique particularly helpful; others will experiment with one, then
another. All are available to try. It is often about finding
"what works". The case studies will be helpful too.

The Term "Survivor"

Throughout the book, I have used the term "survivor". It refers simply to the fact that whatever traumatic event that you have been a victim of/that has befallen you, you have survived it.

Sometimes, survivor may have a slightly different meaning to "survivor", within the Victim–Survivor–Thriver continuum as outlined in Appendix D.

Deliberately, I have avoided using any other term which has negative connotations or is in some way disempowering.

Acknowledgements

First, I would like to thank Steve de Shazer, the co-founder of Solution-Focused Brief Therapy, who inspired me to get involved in this specialist area of work following a two-day workshop he presented in London in the early 1990s.

Second, I would like to thank Yvonne Dolan, a fellow survivor and thriver, who has devoted a large part of her life to working with survivors of severe trauma and stress. In the early days, Yvonne's help to me through her workshops, her writing (N.B.: *Beyond Survival: Living Well is the Best Revenge*), and her personal words of encouragement provided me with great impetus to get more involved in this important work. This was both for my work as a psychotherapist and a trainer.

I am grateful as ever to my wife Lynn who periodically has suggested I write this book due to "the need that is out there". She has been very understanding of my wish to "go away to the coast and write". She has worn well the mantle of "wordsmith's widow".

I am grateful also to Dr Alasdair Macdonald for his encouragement and support with this new project. This came first in the form of inspiring articles, suggestions of new avenues to explore and in the form of useful books loaned. His permission to reproduce a short form evaluation list from his website (www.solutionsdoc.co.uk), thus sharing the evidence base for SFBT, was much appreciated (see Appendix I).

I would like to thank Dr Harry Procter for casting his eye over later drafts of the manuscript and for making some useful suggestions on both design and content.

I am very grateful to my secretary, Joy Minnitt for working on the second and third drafts of the manuscript and to my former secretary, Alison Wright, for the first draft.

Finally, I would like to thank my many clients over the past 25 years who have applied the many techniques within the book to their lasting benefit. The results they achieved surprised them greatly. In the early days, I confess I was surprised too!

About the Author

John Henden, BA (Hons) RMN Dip. Couns. (University of Bristol) MBACP FRSA, is an adult survivor of severe and enduring childhood abuse and neglect. He has had numerous traumatic experiences as an adult, including a near-drowning, three road traffic crashes and hold-up at knife point in a mental hospital. These numerous experiences went unresolved and undeclared for many years; no surprise, therefore, that he experienced numerous bouts of acute depression. Through a combination of self-help and psychotherapy, not only could he declare himself a "survivor", but has gone on to be a "thriver" (see Appendix D).

John has a background in psychology and is a solution-focused therapist, having specialised in severe trauma and stress recovery for nearly 25 years. Also, in addition to being an author, he is a mental health consultant, visiting university lecturer, workshop presenter, and a performance coach.

John is a regular presenter at European Brief Therapy Association conferences and was a founder member of Solutions in Organisations Link-up. During the past 15 years, he has worked in over 20 countries.

He has worked in mental health, welfare and psychological support services for nearly 40 years, having gained both a deep knowledge and a wide experience of "what works", when it comes to helping individuals get their lives back on track. Throughout his career, he has never lost sight of the potential in people to make the necessary changes to live useful and productive lives, despite earlier debilitating labels they may have been given. In addition to Solution-Focused Severe Trauma and Stress Recovery, John's other specialist interest subjects are Healthy Work–Life Balance (stress awareness and management) and Suicide Prevention: the solution-focused approach.

With all the above, John feels more than a little qualified to write this book.

Contents

Section 1

Dealing with "Triggers"

1. "That was then, this is NOW!"
2. "This is normal…"
3. "Breathe it away…"
4. Welcoming triggers through "mindfulness"
5. 5-4-3-2-1 Method

A trigger is something (e.g. a sight, sound, smell, taste or bodily sensation) which sets off a reaction, taking you back to a particular event or situation. Triggers are highly unpredictable. Fighting, fearing, freezing or fleeing from triggers *do not work* in the long term. It is better to *face* them and deal with them. So instead of going for avoidance, go for acceptance. Dealing with them takes out their sting and enables us to remain in control. Also, it prevents the trigger developing into a full-on "flashback" (see Section 2).

The strong suggestion in this manual is not to run from or try to avoid triggers, but to *welcome* them. This allows us to take control, practise the necessary techniques, and to gain mastery over them. The result is often (surprise, surprise!) that the triggers occur less often, and when they do occur, they are dealt with easily and effectively. Welcoming them enables us to expose ourselves to events or situations, in a way that is not harmful and to live our lives to the full, regardless.

The Tools and Techniques

1. "That was then, this is NOW!"

This technique is very powerful for arresting a trigger in its tracks. It ensures the control remains with the survivor and not with the trigger, which could develop easily into a flashback.

The secret is to practise saying, **"That was then, this is *NOW*…!"** on a regular basis, so that it is ready to use in an instant. It is important for workers in this session to encourage survivors to slow down their pace of speech, lower their tone of voice and to say the sentence *forcefully*, with the emphasis on the *"NOW…!"*

With this technique held in readiness, triggers — which are highly unpredictable — need not be feared, instead, they may be *welcomed*.

"Bring on the triggers!"

One survivor who had been traumatised over a number of years, reported that, on average, he encounters one trigger roughly every two weeks, but that this is not a problem now. By using this technique for just a few seconds on each and every occasion, he continues to live life to the full, regardless. He added that he looks forward now to the triggers occurring, so he can both practise and prove to himself that the technique works, *and* to experience being in control.

"The smell of the pork ribs"

A firefighter, who had been involved in attending a house fire where several occupants had died after being badly burned said that, as a result, he had avoided going to barbecues. He found the smell of the cooking meat — especially where pork ribs had been provided — just too much to bear. Clearly, he had been missing out on many potentially enjoyable family and other social gatherings for a few years.

Although avoiding barbecues to which he had been invited, he could not avoid the smell of his neighbours' barbecues, wafting across his back yard, when they chose to have one.

By learning and practising "That was then, this is *NOW*…!", in addition to accepting invitations to others' barbecues, he proved he had gained full control of his trigger by holding one of his own.

2. "This is normal…"

Another way to gain mastery over a trigger is to train the survivors to say quietly and firmly to themselves: "THIS IS NORMAL…" Instruct them as soon as the trigger is observed to become consciously aware of it, to see it for what it is, and to say to themselves: "This is normal. These experiences occur from time to time. I am noticing it fully. And, it will pass." In addition to this statement being so simple and easy to learn, it has great reassurance value.

"Gunfire — no problem"

A soldier, who had returned from a six-month tour of duty in Afghanistan, happened to be walking his dog along a riverside path, well out in the country. Suddenly, he heard the sound of short bursts of machine gunfire from an Army barracks in the distance. Naturally, thoughts of Afghanistan entered his head rapidly and he found himself in a sticky situation on one particular occasion. He was able to prevent this trigger developing into a full-blown flashback by calmly and firmly saying out loud, "This is normal. I am bound to hear the sound of gunfire or other similar sounds from time to time, when I am out and about near military bases."

3. "Breathe it away"

This is another powerful technique for gaining control over triggers. Often, triggers can lead to the survivor taking a sharp in-breath. As is described below, this technique enables survivors to maintain control by controlling their breathing. As a welfare worker/practitioner, you can provide the instruction which follows:

> When the trigger occurs, take control firstly by naming the experience (sight, sound, smell, taste, bodily sensation) as a trigger. Then slowly breathe out, using your diaphragm. (This means ensuring your stomach goes in on the out-breath and out on the in-breath). Often referred to as 7–11 breathing, this is simple. Breathe in through the nose, slowly and gently in, for the count of 7 (ensuring that your stomach goes out on the in-breath). Then, breathe out through the mouth, for the count of 11. Practise this for a couple of minutes about six or seven times a week, over a six- to eight-week period. This ensures it is bedded in fully as a technique for you to use at any time. It is worth practising this type of breathing under normal circumstances anyway, when no triggers are in sight. Not only will you be ready for the trigger when it occurs, but you will feel good, generally, and it is effective for several reasons. Firstly, toxins from the depth of the lungs are expelled on the out-breath. Secondly, the internal organs are massaged by this type of (correct) breathing. Thirdly, because we feel better physically, we feel more relaxed mentally.

This type of breathing is widely recommended for people who want to get control back for themselves when they are feeling out of control. Also, those who experience panic attacks find this technique highly beneficial.

"Breathing away loud bangs"

A woman, who had been within 200 yards of a terrorist's bomb blast that killed and injured dozens, was affected by any loud crash or bang she heard. Most often, it would be dustbins being dropped to the ground, objects being thrown into metal skips or up-and-over garage doors slamming.

After regular practice, she was able to switch instantly from the sharp in-take of breath, to a slow out-breath, then follow the 7–11 breathing routine described above.

4. Welcoming triggers through "mindfulness"

- This fits well with replacing avoidance with acceptance, as outlined in the introduction to this section.

The technique counters powerfully the "fight or flight" response, by disarming it. This is how it works:

At the first whiff of a trigger, say "Ah. I recognise you!", "Welcome!", etc. This response is the complete opposite to trying to run from it or push it down or away. Simply acknowledge the trigger. Pause for a moment and now breathe gently for five times. It may help if you put a hand on your stomach to slow things down. Be aware of that breathing. Now, let the thought come. Do not develop it, let it be. What would help *at this moment?*

You will know. Stay with it. Now carry on with gentle breathing, being in the moment. You may choose now to use techniques, 1, 2 or 3 above, or the mindfulness may be sufficient itself.

5. The 5-4-3-2-1 Method

The procedure outlined below is very useful for dealing with triggers, pulling survivors back to the here and now.

(Also, it is good for inducing sleep if woken at night by internal or external events: see Section 4)

The steps are as follows:

Open your eyes.
Notice five things that you can see.

Close your eyes.
Notice five things that you can hear.
Notice five things that you feel in your body (e.g. warmth, pillows, etc., not emotions).

Open your eyes.
Notice four things that you can see.

Close your eyes.
Notice four things that you can hear.
Notice four things that you feel in your body.

Open your eyes.
Notice three things that you can see.

Close your eyes.

Notice three things that you can hear.

Notice three things that you feel in your body.

Open your eyes.

Notice two things that you can see.

Close your eyes.

Notice two things that you can hear.

Notice two things that you feel in your body.

Open your eyes.

Notice one thing that you can see.

Close your eyes.

Notice one thing that you can hear.

Notice one thing that you feel in your body.

Repeat if necessary to extinguish the trigger more firmly.

After using the exercise four or five times, it will become easier and the calming effect will be greater.

How to Deal with Flashbacks

1. **"Shrinking" (or "the reversing technique")**
2. **Dual awareness**
3. **The rewind technique**
4. **Confronting the flashbacks head-on**
5. **Eye movement desensitisation and reprocessing (EMDR)**
6. **Voluntarily, bring on a pleasant flashback**

Definition of a Flashback: "a recurrence of a memory, feeling or perceptual experience from the past." (DSM-V)

Flashbacks, which are normal, may be triggered by sights, sounds, smells or feelings. The aim is to disrupt these triggers in their tracks by using the techniques in

Section 1 to avoid a resulting flashback. Using techniques for flashbacks can be described as a "second line of defence". Unless we deal with them effectively, as they arise, flashbacks can cause us to feel trapped, powerless, and/or out of control. We may feel at the mercy of our experiences. *This need not happen*, as will be seen in the following pages.

The tools and techniques for dealing with them are easy to learn and easy to apply.

In addition to negative flashbacks, there can be positive ones too, which can bring about pleasant experiences. We can induce these voluntarily and consciously to demonstrate to ourselves that not only can we be in control but that pleasant flashbacks are possible.

We do this by calling up triggers into the past in the form of a pleasant sight, sound, touch, taste or smell. A case example of this can be seen below.

There follows a good selection of techniques to deal with flashbacks into unpleasant experiences. What is of fundamental importance is to arrest the flashback in its tracks so as to minimise its effects.

The Tools and Techniques

1. "Shrinking" (or, "the reversing technique")

The "shrinking" technique is a powerful and effective way for tackling flashbacks in cases where the experience is one of approaching missiles of whatever type. It has been used most effectively for military personnel who have had battlefield experiences of this type, and for vehicle drivers involved in serious road traffic incidents, where debris from other vehicles or complete vehicles themselves have come towards them at speed.

The effectiveness of this technique, like so many others, is attributable to the regaining of power and control. Instead of the distressing psychological and physical sequence of events that might be experienced, survivors take control and "dispose" of the incoming missile in a novel, safe and more comfortable way. Over time, this reduces the severity of the flashback's effects until it has no power left at all.

This is easy for practitioners to teach, and easy for survivors to learn by themselves.

Instruction for the technique is as follows:

"What I invite you to do is to visualise the missile coming towards you. As it approaches you are able to get a good look at it… At the moment before impact, in your mind's eye… stop the missile in its tracks… Now send it back in a different direction towards the distant *horizon*. As it travels this new path*, change its colour to any colour* you choose… As it travels further away, notice how much *smaller* it gets… until it becomes a mere speck on the horizon. If you keep watching, you will notice you cannot see it any longer."

"It is important to practise this at least three times/ week for about 6 weeks. If, on some weeks you manage two practice sessions instead of three, that is okay. As you practise, notice the ways in which you find it helpful or useful."

After practising this technique on a number of occasions, some survivors rename it as "the reversing technique".

"The car wreckage missile — sorted"

An experienced driver of 40-ton, 6-axle lorries, was involved in a fatal road crash, in which three car passengers in two separate vehicles were killed.

A car, which had been overtaking him, crashed head-on into the path of an oncoming lorry, some 40 yards distant. The impact speed was in the region of 100–110 mph. A front wheel of the overtaking car, with attached steering rods, flew through the air at great speed towards the driver's windscreen, hitting it with a giant "thwack!", before bouncing off and away. He knew he would have been killed if the windscreen had smashed. Triggers into flashbacks of this event for this driver were seeing windscreens of passing lorries, department store windows bulging slightly as a result of doors opening and closing, traffic passing, or the wind.

Initially, he tried dealing with the triggers by "That was then, this is *NOW*…!", and before he had mastered this technique for triggers, early on, he found that the full flashback was occurring at speed, so he practised the "shrinking technique" at a regular time each day for a few weeks. This enabled him to have control over both the trigger, and the full flashback to the crash should it occur again. He could have control over it by changing it in the way outlined above. The result was that the flashbacks were less severe and became infrequent. They stopped altogether after about 4–5 months.

2. Dual awareness[a]

This powerful technique has the following instructions. When learning it, make sure you say the words slowly, deliberately and with a strong voice:

"It seems we have got two things going on here."

Right now, I am feeling (isolated/lonely/fearful/etc.[a]) and I am sensing in my body… (3 or so things, i.e. heart racing, perspiring, tremulousness, etc.[a])

These are real sensations — that's what I am experiencing right now — because I am remembering the traumatic event/explosion/incident/abuse/hold-up/assault/robbery/accident/etc.[a]

However, at the same time, I am looking around where I am now here (the place/room[a] where I am now) and:

I can see 5 things…	(name them)
I can hear 5 things…	(name them)
I can sense the following 5 things…	(name them)

And so I know the traumatic event/explosion/incident/abuse/hold-up/assault/robbery/accident/etc.[a] is not happening now or anymore.

---

[a]Adapted from a protocol drawn up by Rothschild (2000). *Note*: Delete the words which do not apply to you; adding others, as appropriate. If you are a practitioner, it is helpful to have this Dual Awareness technique on a database for you to adapt to each client's unique situation.

"Fireworks: where did they come from!"

A veteran of the first Gulf War was walking through his local park one summer's evening, as a "Prom in the Park" was coming to its closing stages. A few minutes later, for him, all hell seemed to break loose as the firework display began with a flash and a bang.

Immediately, he had the beginnings of a full-blown flashback of being in Saudi Arabia, where an incoming Iraqi SCUD missile exploded into a hangar, a few dozen yards from him.

He applied the **Dual Awareness Technique**, as follows:

"It seems we have got 2 things going on here. **Right now** I am feeling terrified and am sensing in my body my heart racing, eyes wide and alert, tightening of my stomach, and sweaty hands. I am wanting to run and take cover.

These are real sensations — that is what I am experiencing right now — because I am remembering the SCUD missile attack all those years ago.

However, at the same time, I am looking around where I am now here in the park and,

I can see 5 things:

— The orchestra playing;
— The smiling, delighted faces of the audience;
— The beautiful colours of the fireworks;
— The moon, partially covered by clouds;
— The grass looking everywhere quite a deep dark green.

I can hear 5 things:

— The whoosh of the rockets, as they rush heavenwards;
— The pleasant sound of some violins;
— The chatter of groups of friends gathered watching;
— The clinking of bottles with wine glasses;
— The distant hum of the evening traffic.

I can sense the following 5 things:

— The smell of the firework smoke;
— The gentle breeze on the side of my face;
— My shoes against the soft turf of the park;
— The sulphurous taste of the smoke;
— My left thumb struggling to get out through the hole in my glove!

And so I know, the SCUD attack in Saudi Arabia is not happening now or any more."

Once the exercise had been completed, the war veteran wandered on, taking in the atmosphere of both the concert and the fireworks, having regained his composure and control.

3. The rewind technique[b]

The rewind technique should be learned and practised under the guidance of an experienced practitioner and

---

[b]This technique was developed by Richard Bandler, of NLP fame. He, in turn, got it from Milton Erickson, who invited clients to look at themselves inside a crystal ball. Griffin & Tyrrell (2004) have developed the idea into an even more powerful form.

works in around 90% of cases. It is carried out in a state of deep relaxation or trance.

Once relaxed, clients are asked to recall or imagine a place where they feel totally safe and at ease. This is their special place. Their relaxed state is then deepened. They are then asked to imagine that, in their special place, they have a TV set and a DVD player with a remote-control facility. Next, they are asked to float to one side of themselves, out of body, and watch themselves watching the traumatic event on the TV (this is a means of creating significant emotional distance). Then they are asked to rewind the trauma as if in real life. Then, they relive it as if in real life (this sets up the "kinaesthetic visualisation"). The film begins at a point before the trauma occurred — a point of safety — and ends at a point at which the trauma is over and they feel safe again. They then float back into their body and imagine pressing the DVD rewind button on the remote control such that they see themselves very quickly going backwards through the trauma from safe point to safe point. Then they watch the same images, but going forwards very quickly, as if pressing the fast forward button.

All this is repeated back and forth, at a speed dictated by the individual concerned and as many times as needed, until the scenes evoke no emotion. They are asked to go forwards and backwards for about four times, which seems, in most cases, to be sufficient in dealing with the traumatic memory.

If it is desirable to instil confidence for facing the feared circumstance in the future — for instance, driving a car or using a lift — they are asked to imagine a scenario in which they are doing so, and feeling confident and relaxed. Once accomplished, clients are brought out of trance, and the work or the rewind technique is complete.

Besides being safe, quick, painless and side-effect free, the technique has the advantage of being non-voyeuristic. Intimate details do not have to be voiced. It is the client who watches the "film", not the worker.

4. Confront the flashbacks head-on

If, on this occasion, you have not succeeded in identifying and dealing successfully with the trigger, say to yourself the following:

"Okay, so this is a flashback. But, I know deep down, the worst is over because the feeling and sensations I am having, are in the past."

"I am here, now, in the present, so let's get the control back!"

Four simple steps to do this are as follows:

1. Pinch yourself, or press one foot on top of the other
2. Breathe normally, overemphasising the out-breaths and in-breaths. Breathe on the out-breath to the count of 11, and on each in-breath to the count of 7 (ensure you use your diaphragm when breathing, as described under "Triggers" above).
3. Re-establish yourself in the present by using the five senses:
    i. I can see 5 things…
    ii. I can hear 5 things…

iii. I can feel 5 things...

iv. I can taste, smell or sense 5 things...

4. Notice in which particular ways you are regaining control.

5. Voluntarily, bring on a pleasant flashback

We have all got a wonderful collection of fond or happy memories from the past. Whether this be from early child-hood, teenage years or more recently. This is a good opportunity to prove you can be in control at will. Bring on one of these pleasant flashbacks by a particular sight, memory, smell, taste, or sensation. By doing this for ourselves, we are then more able to describe its benefits and to be able to teach it to others.

"The sweet perfume of roses"

An adult survivor of severe and enduring multiple child abuse remembered a regular summer holiday staying in a small guest house at a coastal resort. Although he was abused by both parents and they abused each other emo-tionally, this was an annual, relatively "happy" window in each unhappy year.

The proprietor's main passion was to cultivate rare varieties of garden rose. The young boy seldom missed a daily opportunity to take a deep nose-full of scent from the roses of so many vivid colours. Over many years since, he had indulged himself in sniffing garden roses whenever the opportunity presented itself.

He enabled the trigger (the roses' scent) to develop into a full-blown flashback to the many happy holidays of his childhood by the sea.

6. Eye movement desensitisation and reprocessing (EMDR)[c]

This form of treatment has helped hundreds of thousands worldwide, who have suffered from a wide range of traumatic events.

EMDR involves stimulating eye movement in such ways that the brain's information processing systems are stimulated. Amazingly, negative internal messages are squashed instantly, while the person's eyes flicker back and forth, side to side, while focusing on the painful memory.

The instructions for survivors are as follows:

1. I want you to sit comfortably in front of me.
2. Now, for about a minute, shift your eyes rapidly from side to side, while focusing on the incident. Use your closed fist with two fingers up in a V sign, about a foot in front of you, moving side to side to help keep your eyes on track.

---

[c] Some warnings about EMDR: With some individuals, there is a risk of dizziness with this technique. So those, who get dizzy easily, are not advised to use it. Often, this technique can be very effective in removing symptoms in the short term, but they can resurface again unexpectedly later on. You will then need to repeat the exercise. Like all the tools and techniques within this book, this is another for your toolbox, for you to try out.

3. Continue with this pendulum action with your hand for the full minute, focusing fully on the incident.

4. Towards the end of the minute, picture mentally the worst part of the incident. Now, focus on the worst part of the incident, while continuing to shift your eyes in this lateral position.

5. With the image clearly in focus and eyes shifting back and forth, feel your entire body engulfed in panic.

6. Take full account of how your discomfort is spreading from top to bottom and allow it to flow freely without resisting.

7. Now, stop the anxiety abruptly, by taking a deep breath, using your diaphragm to do so.

8. Stop the mental image.

9. Focus on the left and right movement of your two fingers, concentrating on them fully.

10. You will notice, hypnotically, that you will feel less anxiety and be more entranced in pacing your eyes as your two fingers shift back and forth.

11. Focus on the left and right movement of your two fingers, concentrating on them fully.

How to Deal with Unwelcome Thoughts

1. The "Stop!" technique and replaying the DVD later
2. Tackle the guilt trip
3. Tell it — don't bottle it
4. Get in some "degrimming" or black humour
5. The letter from the future
6. Changing the mind-set
7. How to beat the "If only..." monster on the shoulder
8. Write, read and burn
9. "Park it... and move on..."

10. "Let it go… Let it go… Let it go…"
11. Fast Forwarding the DVD of Your Life
12. Ways to deal with anger build-ups
13. Change your mental attitude to the unwelcome thoughts
14. Visualisation
15. The solution-focused feelings tank

Intrusive (or unwelcome or unwanted) thoughts are common in all people. They are thoughts that find their way, often repeatedly, into our everyday thinking. They may develop into "flashbacks" mentioned above, or simply can be irritating and annoying interruptions into whatever we are doing at the time. They can prevent us from having happy and fulfilled lives. In order to stop them causing us emotional or psychological distress, we must deal with them effectively.

The following are many useful tools and techniques for helping survivors to combat these unwanted thoughts. Then they will be able to get on with whatever activity they are involved in, with little or no disturbance.

1. The "Stop!" technique and replaying the DVD later

This technique is very powerful for dealing with regularly occurring intrusive thoughts.

Intrusive thoughts are unpredictable and can occur any time during waking hours: from the very point of waking until last thing at night, as you drift off to sleep.

The "Stop!" technique addresses the issues of both "control" and "boundarying", as to start with, there are no boundaries to the experiences.

First, the survivor needs to make a decision to take control. This is done by wearing a rubber band on a wrist of their choosing. The rubber band should be neither too tight, nor too loose, such that it can be worn comfortably without causing a red mark. The ideal band is the very thin variety as it produces a more painful sting on the inside of the wrist, when pinged.

Once applied to the wrist, the survivor is invited to practise pinging the rubber band. (It is more effective if the practitioner demonstrates it with his own band first, so that they model the experience of both the pinging and the pain.)

The instructions are as follows:

1. As soon as the intrusive thought occurs, reach for the rubber band, and ping it against the inside of your wrist, at the same time saying "Stop!".
2. As you say "Stop!", you are also thinking to yourself "I will give the incident some thinking time later".
3. Carry on with whatever you were doing or thinking about before the intrusive thought occurred.
4. Continue using the "Stop!" technique throughout the day every time the intrusive thought occurs.
5. At a time in the early evening (at least two hours before bedtime), spend 20–30 minutes replaying the incident, as if you were watching it all on a DVD. Begin at a

Sec. 3

point where all was safe, peaceful and quiet before the incident. Then, go through each aspect of the incident, to its end and then to the point where safety, peace and quiet are restored.

6. Repeat this process every day for as long as is necessary.

(N.B.: It is important to "replay the DVD" at least 2 hours before retiring to bed, so that the person can be involved in other thoughts and activities before bedtime. This minimises the risk of the incident's contents being worked out in dreams or nightmares.)

There have been some amazing results achieved with this twin technique. Intrusive thoughts have been reduced from around 80–90 per day down to 5–6 per week, within about five weeks.

While at first survivors have been keen to spend a full 20–30 minutes on the "replay" stage, eventually they find they need less time. Also, the repetition becomes boring and they stop altogether. This is okay, as it demonstrates it has served its purpose.

While some reddening of wrists occurs in the early days of "Stop!", the need to use it lessens, as the brain learns it gets punished when thinking about the incident outside the boundaried time in the early evening.

"The robbery: conquering the aftermath"

A female university student, who was earning extra cash by working evening shifts in her local "off licence", was the victim of an armed robbery, as she was cashing up at 10 pm. Two balaclava-clad men rushed in, pointing a handgun at her, demanding the day's takings and several hundred cigarettes. For a couple of weeks, she had a recurrent nightmare and was having up to 80 intrusive thoughts per day, involving particularly their wild looking eyes and the shiny parts of the handgun.

After using the "Stop!" technique for one week, the intrusive thoughts had reduced to 4–5 per day and the nightmares had all but stopped.

With the "replaying of the DVD" part of this technique, more power can be provided by adding in "the paper strips method". The instruction for this runs as follows:

1. Fold five sheets of A4 size white paper horizontally into half.
2. Press hard along the crease with your thumbnail, before tearing the five sheets in half. This provides two lots of five sheets (now A5 size).
3. Fold each new set of A5 sheets in half again horizontally.
4. Repeat as before, tearing along the crease.
5. Continue this process until you have 40 (5 × 8) strips of paper.
6. Fold two sheets of coloured A4 size paper, horizontally, as above.
7. Continue tearing, folding and tearing, until these two sheets have produced 16 strips.

Sec. 3

8. Now, with step 5 above, replay the incident, beginning with what you were doing before it began.
9. With each part of the story, place one white strip on a table.
10. Place a coloured strip, each time you remember something you did well: a personal quality/strength/ characteristic that you brought into play, or something you were pleased about.
11. Continue the process, right through the incident and on to the point that equilibrium was restored, or a point of safety was reached.
12. You should end up with a giant multi-layer paper strip sandwich of both the white and coloured paper strips. Usually, survivors end up using white strips to coloured strips, to a ratio of about 4:1.

There is a three-fold purpose to adding "the paper strips method" to this technique:

A. It reduces the risk of retraumatisation, as strengths, qualities and other positive points punctuate the story.
B. It empowers the survivor, as they are taking more control of the story, while they replay the DVD to themselves.
C. It speeds up the time when boredom kicks in. The brain will, literally, become fed up with having to go through this exercise day after day, and will be wanting to be occupied with something else more interesting.

This "Stop!" technique and replaying the DVD later, along with the paper strips, has been highly effective in reducing intrusive or unwelcome thoughts for many people.

It is best illustrated by the following example.

A lorry driver had been travelling along a bending section of single carriageway bypass, when he noticed a motorcyclist travelling towards him. Being a motorcyclist himself, he thought that the motorcyclist was going too fast for the bend, and his positioning on his side of the road was not good.

The lorry driver slowed to about 40 mph, hoping the motorcyclist would slow down, too. Within seconds, he saw the motorcyclist's terrified expression, as he hit the front of the cab at an impact speed of in excess of 90 mph. For about a week after the incident, the driver was having 70–80 flashbacks per day. Adding the paper strips method to replaying the DVD, the exercise went as follows:

— "There I was driving along the open road, at a steady 50 mph.

— lays down one white strip (WS).

— The sun was shining and there were a few puffy white clouds in the sky.

— WS

— I was listening to a play on Radio 4, and, being mid p.m., there was not much traffic about.

— WS

— I could see a motorcyclist at about 200 yards away, coming towards me. He seemed to be going too fast for the curve.

— WS

— I slowed down to about 40 mph, as he continued to approach at speed.

— lays down green strip (GS)

— He was still coming fast into the curve and both his road positioning and "lean", was all wrong.

— WS

— He was coming straight towards my cab, I braked sharply and safely, slowing fast.

— GS

— I saw his terrified expression and he seemed to be mouthing the words "Oh God!"

— WS

— There was a terrific bang and a jolt to my cab. I travelled a bit further, scraping wreckage until I brought my vehicle to a halt.

— WS

— I put the lorry into gear, applied the handbrake, turned off the ignition, picking up my mobile phone and stepped down from the cab.

— GS

Sec. 3

— I took a quick glance at the mangled bike wreckage and the dead rider. He was beyond help.

— WS

— I phoned 999, giving them an accurate position of the incident.

— GS

— Other vehicles had slowed down and stopped.

— WS

— Already there was one driver, directing traffic.

— WS

— I informed the other drivers and passengers, who were approaching, to stay away from the front of the lorry, for their own benefit. There was nothing to be done for the rider, and, anyway, the emergency services were on their way.

— GS

— Another two drivers agreed to direct traffic.

— WS

— I returned to my cab, to phone my transport manager, to inform him of events.

— GS

— I switched the radio over to a music channel, to try and calm my nerves, while waiting for the emergency services to arrive.

— GS

Sec. 3

— The Police arrived first.

> — WS

— I got down from the cab and locked it behind me, in accordance with my driving rules.

> — GS

— I sat in the Police car and made a statement.

> — WS

— I noticed the ambulance arrive. They removed the body.

> — WS

— As the policeman was finishing his interview, I heard a fire and rescue tender arrive, at the same time that the breakdown vehicle joined the scene.

> — WS

— I returned to the cab to remove all personal items and my company documents that may have been under the dashboard.

> — GS

— I had a lift in the police patrol car back to my home.

> — WS

— On the way, he said his colleague would be at the scene for some time, measuring skid marks on the road, etc.

— WS

— On the way, the policeman chatted, reassuringly. He was a kind bloke and gave me a cup of hot, sweet tea from his own flask.

— GS

— He told me that he sees too many motorcycle fatalities, in the course of his work.

— WS

— Once home, I had a hot bath. I chucked in loads of bath salts and lay there for about an hour-and-a-half.

— GS

— I dressed and went downstairs to the kitchen. I made myself a large mug of cocoa. All I could eat was a bowl of soup and some dry bread.

— GS

— I sat in my lounge, trying to watch some TV, before going to bed.

— WS"

Sec. 3

2. "Tackle the guilt trip"

Two common unwelcome thoughts in many survivors of severe trauma are guilt and self-blame. Questions which keep intruding into the waking mind are: "I feel so guilty because I survived and he died", "Things went wrong and I am to blame", "I feel so bad about it and it's all my fault!", "My concentration dipped only for a few seconds. If only I had….. it wouldn't have happened!", etc.

When disturbing things like this have happened to us, it is quite normal to have these intrusive guilt or self-blaming thoughts. It is often referred to as "survivor guilt".

There are two ways to deal with these.

(a) *"It was not your fault"*

First, tell yourself it was *not your fault* or you are not to blame. In most situations, even though we do feel guilty, when we look at the hard facts, we discover we are not to blame and in no way, was it our fault. Give the incident/ situation a reality check.

"It was my fault the baby was killed"

A 19-year-old woman in a war zone was held captive in some farm buildings by about a dozen occupying troops. There were some 25 fellow captives, one of them carrying a six-month-old baby. The baby was crying because it was hungry, so after dark, the teenager crept over into an enclosure of dairy cows, milking one of them, so the baby could be fed. Once she arrived back, she was discovered by two of her captors, who promptly killed the baby in punishment for the theft of the milk. For over 40 years, she told no one, carrying an enormous burden of guilt over the baby's death. It was not surprising that during that time she had experienced much anxiety, depression and sleep disturbance.

Her therapist helped her look at the facts:

— She felt normal human compassion towards both the mother and her hungry baby.
— It was an act of human kindness to look for food to ease the baby's obvious distress.
— She ventured bravely into the night to milk one of the cows.
— The two occupying troops should take full responsibility for their cruel actions; she was not to blame.
— The troops took the decision to kill the baby and not the young woman for the theft.
— No one can ask more than for us to do our best at the time, in any set of circumstances we find ourselves in.

A final question which proved very helpful was:

"What skills, qualities and resources did you bring to the fore to get through that ordeal at the time and over the ensuing months, until the end of the war?"

Over the final three sessions the guilt fell away and she felt much freer. At the last session, she resolved to fulfil a lifelong dream of working with brain-injured children.

Sec. 3

(b) *"You are not wholly to blame"*

In some situations, or with some incidents, after taking a long hard look at the facts, we may discover we were to blame, to some extent. The question to ask is, "Were you 100% to blame?" You will find, in every case, the answer is "No", as there is always someone else to share it.

This is illustrated best with the following example.

"I should have saved my son from suicide"

A divorced man in his fifties had three grown up children. His son, who was his middle child, was living alone in a bedsitting room. He had experienced depressive episodes for a number of years, having sought help from his GP on several occasions. Each time, he had been prescribed pills. Six months previously, he had spent a month or so in a local psychiatric inpatient facility but discharged himself because, "… they just gave me more pills and observed me. The staff, apart from telling me where to go and what to do, didn't really seem to want to talk to me".

Over one long weekend, the man's son took his life by swallowing all his prescribed medication.

With the help of his counsellor, the father, who felt he was totally responsible for his son's death ("If I had been a better father …", "I should have gone round to see him more often …", "I could have paid for some decent counselling for him…, etc.), could appreciate that others shared the blame. With the counsellor's help, he came up with the following other people and their approximate percentages of the total blame:

The GP for prescribing pills only, and not referring him to a reputable counsellor: 30%

The psychiatrist who carried medical responsibility for his son's treatment in hospital: 30%

The nursing staff on the unit who seemed to want minimal interactions only with inpatients: 20%

His son for not pressing his case for better help: 10%

Politicians for underfunding Mental Health Services: 20%

Manufacturers of psychiatric drugs, who convince doctors that their products are treatment rather than (in reality) simply symptom-alleviation: 20%

The community care worker who was supposed to call round to the bedsit to see him following his discharge from the inpatient unit: 15%

Total for "others":   145%!

Sec. 3

This happens often, where the tot-up of the others' percentages exceeds 100%. It can only be 100% in total, *including* the father's percentage. So, pressing him, to take a share of this 100%, helps him accept a realistic percentage of his part in the incident.

Once he had accepted his share, he believed he should carry approximately 20% of the blame. Then he was helped to deal with and come to terms with that 20%. Subsequently, he resolved to join a support group for others bereaved by suicide, as a way of 'paying back'.

3. "Tell it — don't bottle it"

Bottling up, suppressing or pushing down has never done anyone any good. It may help us forget about things in the short term but it is *not good for our health.*

If we push things down for any length of time, they will bubble up in the daytime when we are least expecting it, or will surface at night in the form of vivid dreams and/ or nightmares. Worse: it could come out in some form of psychosomatic problem or physical illness. ("What's pushed down, must come up later.")

We need to express it safely, in some way or another. This may be done either by the spoken word, "writing, reading and burning" or high-energy physical exercise (see both in Sections 4 and 6.)

Some helpful guiding statements are:

- "It's good to talk".
- "A problem shared is a problem halved".

Be careful who you tell

Some people are not able to cope with what they hear, especially if it is either shocking or tragic, or both, so may protect themselves by simply not believing. Others simply will not understand. Some will glaze over as they are told. Still more will show no understanding or empathy while they are being told. Others cannot keep confidences and will be bursting to tell someone else what they have been told.

Finding the right person to share, in complete confidence, what has happened to you, is both rewarding and liberating.

4. "Get in some degrimming or black humour"

The ability to use humour or to "de-grim" situations by some quip or other is a quality which enables people to overcome the most horrendous situations. There are countless examples of how this has been helpful in many situations and with various traumatic events. Black humour has been used to good effect, both during an incident and afterwards. It helps us lighten an otherwise grim situation and helps us deal with it on the spot and to "put it away" more safely in our memory, until such a time when it can be dealt with more effectively, should that be necessary.

Examples

1. Firefighters who attended a fatal car crash: "One thing's for certain: she won't do that again!"
2. Ambulance staff at a failed suicide attempt from a bridge: "As he jumped, he didn't expect his overcoat to balloon out like a parachute!"
3. During an earthquake, a man who ran out of a collapsing building, just in time: "I would have found myself at the Pearly Gates, sooner than I expected!"

Sec. 3

5. "The letter from the future[a]"

This letter is to be written and not posted:

Pick a time in the future: 5, 10, 15, 20 years from now, or any number of years — longer or shorter — that is meaningful to you. Date the top of the letter with the imaginary future date. Imagine that the intervening years have passed and you are writing to a friend (pick someone you know and like in the present time). Use the friend's name: "Dear (friend's name)". Or, if you prefer, pick some other supportive person to whom you can imagine writing to, comfortably.

The purpose of dating the letter and writing it to someone you know, in reality, is to strengthen the psychological realism of the letter for you on both an unconscious level and a conscious level. Imagine that in this future, you have resolved whatever problems that are troubling you at the present time. Describe what helped you resolve those problems. At the time of the letter writing, you are living a wonderful, joyous, healthy and satisfying life. Describe how you are spending your time, where you are living, your relationships, beliefs and reflections on the past and future.

How to use the letter from the future[b]

Now that you have completed the letter, what did you learn? What did you include in the letter that is not yet

---

[a]With full acknowledgement to Milton Erickson for the original version and to Yvonne Dolan for a later amended version.
[b]With full acknowledgement to Yvonne Dolan.

happening in your life? What would be the smallest[c] step in your actual behaviour or reactions that you could take towards making one of those things begin to happen? When do you want to try that step?

What difference would that small step make if it continued over time? Are other small steps needed now? What would be the next smallest one? What will the result(s) be for each of the steps you can identify? When do you want to start? If not, is it the wrong goal? If you want to start, but feel stuck, are there any advantages to not starting? If so, is there some way that some of the advantages of not starting (such as extra time, etc.) could be preserved to some degree without you staying stuck? What will be the consequences (how will you feel in 5, 10, 15, 20 years) if you do not start? The purpose of this question is to identify your motivation. If you still want to start, do not be discouraged by the smallness of steps. If you need inspiration for the power of small steps, go and interview a successful quilt maker, or writer, or tile layer, or anyone who has work that progresses gradually.

Sec. 3

---

[c] Sometimes people ask, "Why imagine the smallest sign, why not big, glorious signs?" The aim here is to make whatever changes you desire become unintimidating, to scale them down to a level that is comfortably achievable for you, so that your goal is reachable. It is not that people fail to make changes because they are lazy. What passes for laziness is usually fear, demoralisation or despair. The smallness of these signs is intended to overcome fear and demoralisation, and to allow you to complete your own version of the proverbial "Chinese Journey of a Thousand Miles", one small achievable step at a time. If the steps you identify seem too small, simply make them slightly larger, taking care to make them no larger than is "do-able" in the next day or two. Then proceed. Remember, if the process stalls, or if you become overwhelmed or stuck, check to see if the goal is truly what you want, and if so, ask yourself if the step needs to be made smaller. Keep making it smaller until it is one you can do. Do not give up; you deserve the life you want.

In fact, what work does not progress gradually? You are your own greatest project!

6. "Changing the mind-set"

This is a useful technique for survivors who have a fixed belief about a situation.

Before changing the (fixed) mind-set, it is important to "loosen the negative thinking around the edges". This means, sowing seeds of doubt about its validity, highlighting strengths, abilities and resources within, and if possible, flagging up how some of these were used in the situation. Also, questions, such as "What would you do more of or do differently next time, should a similar incident occur?" and "What might be the smallest, positive thing you have taken away from the incident?", may be helpful.

Once the edges of the negative thinking have been loosened sufficiently, the following types of statements can be made as appropriate:

1. "You did the best you could under the circumstances."
2. "You were simply doing your job."
3. "You had to think and act quickly. Sometimes in instances such as these, mistakes are made."
4. "It was either you or them: what other choices did you have?"
5. "Sometimes on life's journey, shocking/distressing/frightening/upsetting things like this happen to us. In what ways has this made you a stronger person?"

Sec. 3

6. "It seems you were in the right place at the right time."

7. "It seems you were in the wrong place at the right time."

8. "Sometimes in life, we do something terrible. However, rather than beating ourselves up about it, we can try to forgive ourselves. We may ask for God's forgiveness, too."

9. "With some things that happen, for which we feel responsible, we can pay back in some way by doing good deeds for others. What might you do, if you were so inclined?"

10. "You can either look at your injuries as "the end of the world", or you can decide how you can live life to the full, despite them."

11. "What would you say you have learned as a result of this experience?"

12. Add your own.

13. Add your own.

14. Add your own.

7. How to beat the "If only…" monster on the shoulder

"**If only**…" can be a handicapping recurrent thought for us, in that it has the powerful result of keeping us stuck in the present.

Severe trauma and stress survivors have found this technique both highly effective and fun to do.

The technique for dealing with it is an adaptation of that used by Jacob (2001) when working with eating distress. With this technique, survivors are encouraged to "externalise the problem" by sitting it on their shoulder, such that it can be seen as an object in its own right, rather than as an internal part of them.

Once it is sat on the shoulder, not only can you get a good look at it, in its entirety, but also you can get into direct and assertive conversation with it. The objective of these conversations is to beat it/outsmart it/defeat it/put it on the back foot/etc. Most survivors prefer "beat it" because of the triple meanings of this phrase: "successfully argue against it", "beat it physically", and "persuade it to beat it (leave altogether)."

"If only…", if allowed to persist, is very controlling and disempowering. The survivors must regain both power and control. This technique achieves both.

How is this achieved in actual fact? Sometimes it is helpful for survivors to describe what their **"If only…"** monster looks like once they have taken it out of their body and placed it on their shoulder. The most important part of the technique is the next part, when they come up with three or four things they would like to say to their monster, in order to begin defeating it. Some typical commands are:

"It's happened, and there's nothing anyone can do about it!"

"Shut up! Get out of my life. I'm moving on!"

"Go and take a running jump! And I hope you will kill yourself!"

"I'll give you more than 'if only…', if you don't shut it!"

(And ruder and more explicit commands…!)

As with other techniques, it is helpful if the technique is practised right now. Then, to practise it about 10–12 times/week for a few weeks. This will make sure the power and control is transferred back from "the monster" to yourself.

"Finally, I got rid of my 'If only ...' monster"

A man in his late twenties walked out of a good, well-paid job after an argument with his boss. He was unemployed for a while and was living in very reduced circumstances. His "**If only ...**" monster spoke as follows:

- "If only you hadn't had such a late night before, you wouldn't have been so tired and irritable, when you spoke to your boss",
- "If only you had kept your mouth shut when your boss made that provocative remark!", and
- "If only I had walked away!"

By going through the procedure above, and practising it whenever the "monster" spoke, the man was able to move on. Eventually, he found another job with another company within the same industry.

8. Write, read and burn (or write, read and shred)[d]

Based on a technique from the Milwaukee Brief Therapy Centre, the purpose of this exercise is to resolve any negative memories that are intruding upon and

---

[d]With full acknowledgement to Yvonne Dolan and Charlie Johnson for the original version.

Sec. 3

constricting the person's life in the present, in the form of intrusive thoughts or images.

The instructions are as follows:

A. First of all, write down the details of the memory, thought, or image that troubles you.
B. Now, write down any feelings you have about the memory, thought or image. If another person is involved in the memory, address these feelings to that person, where appropriate. Include anything you would wish to say or wish you could say to that person.
C. Now re-read what you have written, reading it aloud.[e]
D. Once you have done so, burn (or shred) the pages.

9. "Park it… and move on…"

A powerful instruction to the mind for dealing with intrusive thoughts, this technique is a simple statement which acknowledges simply that the incident occurred, without attempting to bury it in any way. This has been of great help to survivors in both civilian and military contexts.

As a car parking metaphor, it is helpful because the survivor can conjure up a picture of parking an old car anywhere they choose (a lay-by, car park, roadside, etc.) — and then walk away from it — and move on, along their life-journey.

They may choose to return to the car, from time to time, either to take a fresh look at it, maybe sit inside for a while, or drive it around a little. In either case, they can

[e]While not essential, sometimes it is helpful psychologically to have another person present (e.g. a friend, relation or counsellor) to hear what you read and witness the burning or shredding of the pages.

park it again — lock it up — move on — returning to their walk along life's journey.

This metaphor is powerful in another way, as what becomes of cars when they are left parked-up and neglected for a long period of time? They become dusty, covered in cobwebs, the tyres deflate and brakes and clutch plates become seized. Eventually they become a rusty heap, fit for scrap only and certainly, after many years, not something you would want to revisit anyway. By this time, a great distance has been covered between the "parked" car and your life-journey. What happens is that, although the car was an important part of your life, its potential to affect you in the present weakens further and further. It begins to become but a distant memory.

It is helpful for the survivor to practice saying this command: **"Park it… and move on…"**, saying it between 10 and 12 times/week, when unwelcome thoughts occur, and then for a number of weeks following to bed-in the technique thoroughly.

10. "Let it go… Let it go… Let it go…"

This technique is very powerful for dealing with intrusive thoughts. Rather than the survivor trying to push down the unpleasant thought when it arises (which, as is well known, *does not work*), the following instruction is given:

1. Acknowledge, briefly, the unpleasant thought.
2. Accept that it is unwelcome and not wanted.
3. Say to yourself, quietly but firmly:

   "Let it go… Let it go… Let it go…"

11. "Fast Forwarding the DVD of Your Life"

Fast forwarding the DVD is used to:

- bypass problem thinking,
- create a context for setting well-formed goals,
- encourage expectations of change,
- get information about *how* you can make progress,
- find out about things you can do, which will get you to where you want to be.

Fast forwarding the DVD

Before counsellors or therapists ask this question, it is important to get a sufficient understanding about the survivor's current difficulties or problem situation.

Next, it is crucial to get their full attention, before asking the question. This is achieved best by adopting a slight air of mystery and then asking, "Can I ask you a rather unusual question. . .?" As a therapist, in my 20 years or so of asking this question, I have yet to have someone say "No, you can't!". As human beings, we are too curious!

Once they have agreed to the question being asked, ensure you *lower your tone of voice* and *slow down you pace of speech*. This is important.

Then, when you have their full attention, ask:

"Just suppose... over there in the corner (look over at corner of the room), there is a TV and DVD player.... In it, there is a DVD of your life in, say, six months' time, when you have got everything sorted.... In my hand there is a remote control or mobile phone (hold an actual remote control) I fast forward the DVD to the point where your difficulty or problem is sorted.... Then I press the 'play' button. What will be the first thing we will see on the TV monitor, to let us know that your difficulty or problem is now solved…?" (Remain still and quiet.)

…What else will we see…?   What else…?

…What will you be doing   What else will
differently…?   you be doing…?

…What different reactions might you see in those closest to you…?

…What else…?

…How will your thinking have changed?   How else…?

Some people find the fast forwarding the DVD question easier to use than others. It involves patience and some creative thinking to get a clear picture of something to do which is realistic, achievable, measurable and something they want to happen.

"I kicked into touch, both the booze and the cigs"

An ex-serviceman, who had been deployed in four theatres of operations over a seven-year career, had been medically discharged due to "alcoholism". He had received detox treatment only before leaving the service. He was referred to an NHS community mental health team for help. The worker found him living in poverty in a small flat which was filthy. Ashtrays piled with cigarette ends, empty wine and spirits bottles adorned most surfaces and he was in a neglected and dishevelled state.

When asked the fast forwarding the DVD question, as above, he answered:

"I will have got control of all this drinking…"

"I will have sorted my life out…"

"I will have this place (looking around) tidied up…"

What else…?:

"The smoking: I'll be down to no more than 5 a-day…"

"Maybe, too, I'll have spoken to those in that help office, at the Regeneration Project…"

And what else…?:

"I can't see myself working yet, but maybe I'll have a few ideas…"

"And…   I'll have sorted my head out more, so I won't need the drink to block it out…Doesn't work for long anyway."

12. Ways to deal with anger build-ups

Anger is a common result of severely traumatic experiences and is quite normal and understandable. It can become a problem if it is not dealt with (i.e. get it out of the way safely, as it starts to build). Anger outbursts can have a catastrophic effect on both property and within relationships. First, we must recognise it. Second, we need to put in a plan of action to deal with it in a safe, healthy and controlled way.

In the following pages are some ideas and some techniques with which to express anger safely and effectively.

There are six main ways:

I. *Chat to a (trusted) friend, colleague, counsellor or therapist*

"A problem shared is a problem halved" is the main principle that works here. Telling someone you can trust and who will keep what you say confidential can be a great relief and a release for any anger build-up.

II. *Write it down*

Many thousands of survivors of traumatic experiences have found it very helpful to write down emerging anger feelings, listing how and from where they have arisen. It is important to write as much as necessary and can be done either on a writing pad, in a journal or personal diary.

Survivors must be encouraged to take great care to keep it confidential. If it is written on loose leaf paper, there is the option always to burn or shred it afterwards. If a journal or personal diary is used, make sure it is kept in a safe and secure place. It is important to be careful what is committed to paper, just in case secrecy and confidentiality are compromised. Using a personal code or abbreviations can be helpful, for when referring to people, places and events.

III. *Do strenuous physical exercise*

Many people have found that strenuous physical exercise has a positive, discharging effect for any anger build-ups. This may involve a workout in the gym, a circuit training round, kicking a football, going for a long cycle ride, jogging, using a punchbag, or anything else which is harmless. With any of us when anger builds, it is best to keep away from others until we have found our own way to discharge it safely. (Being in the presence of others, however close they are to us, can be provocative.) Arguments can arise, which lead to anger spilling over in the direction of people we love and/or hold dear, both in unhealthy or damaging ways.

When encouraging survivors to use this technique, it is helpful for them to explain to those closest to them, their need to be on their own at these times, to get on with their own particular chosen workout. Once those closest understand this, the majority are fine with it. Some couples, especially, have a particular code word they use, for this need for personal space and time, to devote to their chosen method.

"Boxer-cise circuits"

A soldier who had many angry feelings about some situations he had been involved in whilst serving in the second

Gulf War, found it really helpful to do a couple of rounds of "boxer-cise" circuits in the gym, when his anger level builds. His code word to his wife at these times was "build-up". She would reply "okay", and all would be fine once he returned.

IV. *Find somewhere safe to shout it out*!

A number of survivors of severe trauma and stress find it very helpful to shout out as loudly as they can or need to, about things which have caused them to feel angry about a traumatic situation (or situations) they found themselves in. So as not to alarm others(!) — especially those close to them — it is important to find somewhere isolated and safe in which to have a good shout!

Some good examples of places to use are:

- in a parked car, in an isolated spot, with all windows shut firmly,
- along a coastal path or on a beach,
- along a footpath in open country, in between large fields,
- in a sound-proofed room or building,

"My so-called best mate"

A travelling salesman, whose "best mate" had dated his partner while he had been away working, was furious at both his partner and his so-called "best mate". He wanted the relationship to get back on track, and still wanted to be friends with his mate. He knew, initially, it

Sec. 3

would be unwise and unsafe to "have it out" with each of them. So, in order to discharge the overwhelming anger safely, he parked his car in a layby on a rarely used country road, to shout at them, in their absence. He told another mate: "I was quite hoarse when I'd finished, but I felt better!"

A few sessions later, he was able to speak to them individually, in a calm voice and without the risk of violence.

V. *Draw it or paint it*

Some survivors have more artistic leanings and find either drawing or painting very therapeutic. Many find these as good ways to discharge angry (and other negative) feelings.

VI. *Play loudly, your own choice of music*

Playing music loudly can be a good way of getting in touch with strong, angry feelings in order to discharge those feelings. It may be a particular track or a whole album. This can be done at home, out in a car or via a personal sound system (NB: take care not to disturb neighbours or damage your eardrums!).

How to measure the discharge of negative feelings

One very effective way to measure how well you are doing is to use the "solution-focused feelings tank", as shown in Figure 1.

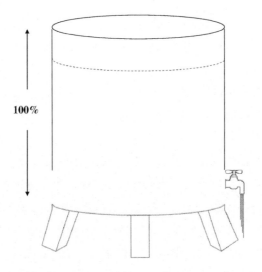

Figure 1.   The solution focused feelings tank.

First, it is important to explain to how the tank may be used. It is in the shape of a garden water butt, containing whatever quantity of the strong negative feeling you may have right now (e.g. anger, disappointment, sadness, shame, guilt, regret, etc.).

The explanation about how to use it is as follows:

1. "There is no inlet pipe, but there is a tap, over which you have control."
2. "You will never empty the feelings tank about this situation completely (i.e. anger in this case), because the tap is at a higher level than the bottom of the tank."
3. "How much anger have you managed to run off through this tap, so far?" (Suppose it is, say, 3%.)
4. "3%! How have you managed to do that?"

5. "What's the next small step you could take to run off another 1% over the next 2–3 weeks?"
6. "And what else could you do, to get the level down by just another 1%?"

    … and so on.

This exercise has proved to be very helpful in empowering survivors to take control of whatever negative feeling keep popping up in the form of unwanted thoughts. It is also a very affirming exercise, as only occasionally will someone answer that their tank is 100% full. The majority of people answer, initially, between 70 and 95%. So, some credit can be given for what actions/changes in thinking, they have taken already.

13. Change your mental attitude to the unwelcome thoughts

- It is the way we respond to unwelcome thoughts that causes us distress.
- It is our reaction which enables these thoughts to have power and influence over us.
- The more we try and push unwelcome thoughts away, the more they will struggle to get back into our conscious mind (e.g. Notice what happens when you tell yourself: "Whatever you do, *do not* think of pink elephants!")
- To prevent ourselves being pestered by unwelcome thoughts, we need to use an effective technique to reduce their frequency.

Survivors can be helped by the following four-step approach to changing your mental attitude:

1. Welcome the intrusive thought (or fear).
2. Imagine a cartoon character (e.g. Tom Cat from Tom and Jerry, or Donald Duck).
3. Give it a squeaky voice.
4. Have the cartoon character speak out the thought (e.g. "Remember that car crash where you slowed down but didn't stop to help the injured?").

The result of the cartoon imagery is to reprogramme the initial fearful emotional reaction — so it takes out the power it had over you. The less you fear the thought, the less likely it is to occur during the day. Thereby, the emotional reaction has been neutralised.

14. Visualisation

This is done best when either sitting or standing and should last from 10 to 15 minutes. It achieves the objective of enabling the service user to regain control over anxious or unwanted thoughts, after it has been practised daily for a few weeks. When performed immediately after the technique mentioned in Section 10 above, it has even more power over anxious thoughts or any type.

The mind needs to release regularly what it is holding on to. When it does, soothing and beneficial results are achieved.

With practise, this technique enables you to release all stress within minutes of starting the exercise. You will have trained your brain. Daily practice before bedtime enables you to sleep more soundly.

Survivors can follow the following instructions:

i. In either the sitting or the standing position, gently move your attention to your breath.

ii. Place one hand on your stomach and the other on your upper chest.

iii. Take in a breath, letting your stomach swell forward as you do so, letting it fall back on the out-breath. (Your hand on your chest should have no or little movement).

iv. Repeat this for three times, lengthening the in-breath to the count of 7, and the out-breath to the count of 11. (This is called 7/11 diaphragmatic breathing and is referred to in other parts of this book). The more you practise 7/11 breathing, the more you will strengthen the diaphragm, and the more it will work how it is meant to, naturally.[f]

v. Now slow it down even more by adding a short pause after the out-breath, before breathing in again. (At first, you might feel you are not getting enough air but with practice, you will become more comfortable with it).

vi. If unwanted or unwelcome thoughts come to mind as you do this, simply let them go on the out-breath, focusing back on your breathing.

---

[f]Wisegeek. What is the Diaphragm Muscle? www.wisegeek.com/what-is-the-diaphragm-muscle.htm (accessed 22 May 2017).

vii. Now, move your attention to your feet, trying to really feel them. See if, one-by-one, you can feel each toe.

viii. Now visualise the soles of your feet with roots growing slowly downwards, deep into the earth beneath. Visualise the roots growing more quickly and firmly now into the earth, so that you are now rooted to the spot like a magnificent oak tree.

ix. Concentrate on this feeling of being grounded securely and safely for a minute or so.

x. Now visualise a cloud of bright light forming up high above you.

xi. Notice now, a bolt of lightening shoots down from the cloud on to the top of your head. As it does, it transforms itself into a circular band of white light which descends slowly down from your head, past your shoulders, waist and legs, down to your toes. As it passes downward, feel it clearing away any rubbish you may have been thinking about, so that now you have a clear and free mental state.

xii. Repeat this image of the circular band of light passing down your body for about five times, until you feel a sense of all anxious thinking being cleared away and released.

xiii. Now, visualise yourself standing under a large luminescent waterfall where you are able to breathe easily.
- The water is bubbling, radiant, cleansing and full of vitality.
- Feel the water, washing down your body, soothing and calming you as it does so.

Sec. 3

  ○ Hear the splash of the water on the ground all around you.
  ○ As you enjoy this experience, even more, tell yourself that not only is the water life itself, but it is washing away any anxiety, stress or worry from both your mind and your body.

xiv. After a few moments, and in your own time, open your eyes. Then, gently and slowly move away to what you were doing before or want to do next. (As you move away, avoid ripping too much of the ground away, as each root is severed!)

This visualisation, like many others, achieves the twin objectives of restoring calm and replacing a sense of lack of control, with one of *control.*

15. The solution-focused feelings tank

Sometimes an intrusive thought is connected to a negative feeling we have about a situation. This negative feeling can be any one or several of the following:

Anger	Hurt	Self-blame
Disappointment	Being overwhelmed	Grief
Fear	Rage	Worthlessness
Guilt	Regret	Confusion
Sadness	Worry	Embarrassment
Shame	Helplessness	Low self-confidence, etc.

If we let them, these negative feelings can take control of us. Therefore, it is important to take the control back. Using the solution focused feelings tank (Figure 1) is very helpful for achieving this.

Sec. 3

Section 4

Dealing with "The Lows"

Sec. 4

1. Work at and maintain a good, healthy balanced diet
2. Drink plenty of liquids
3. Remind yourself of the power of humour
4. Do something pleasurable for the sake of it
5. Build up your physical fitness or a sufficient level of physical activity
6. Keep self-confidence and self-esteem at a high level
7. See "the lows" as a virus which can be dealt with
8. Get out there and get reconnected with supportive people

9. Acknowledge to yourself that you have a touch of "the lows"

10. Increase your knowledge/get more information

11. Get enough sleep

12. "The rainy-day letter"

13. "Don't just lie there, get up!"

14. Breathe your way to a relaxed state

15. What to do if you let "the lows" get too low

One thing is for certain: all survivors will have low days as they make their journey back to full recovery and control. The good news is that, as the tools and techniques in this book are mastered, you will be more in control, more often. This means you will not be controlled by negative thinking and the "lows" that accompany them. However, it is not realistic to think you can prevent all low days. There will be times when you feel you are not getting anywhere, asking questions such as "What is it all about anyway?", "I feel just like giving up!", "I feel I'm back at square one!", etc. It is most helpful to have a plan or strategy ready, for when these days happen. Some practical techniques are as follows.

1. Work at and maintain a good balanced diet

As we are resolving reactions to past events, there can be a tendency to "comfort eat".

This does us no favours at all. Nor does it do any favours to our family and friends, who have to cope with our reduced agility, poorer health, and lower energy levels.

Sec. 4

The trouble is comfort eating tends to consist mainly of all the wrong things: chocolates, sweets, biscuits, fast food and fizzy drinks.

Contrary to some opinions, healthy eating need not be expensive. Often, in fact, it can be cheaper. Ensure you get your "5-a-Day" fruits and vegetables. A healthy intake of the whole range of vitamins and minerals helps towards feeling good. It is sensible to cut down on saturated fats, salt and sugar too.

2. Drink plenty of liquids

Ensuring 2–3 litres of liquids in various forms every day will mean both that you feel better and that your brain and body functions as it should. Headaches, too, can be avoided. A car engine running on little oil will not perform as well as when "full" is seen on the dipstick. Drinking water is preferable, but fruit juice, squash or hot beverages are okay too. With the last three, care needs to be taken about not taking in too much sugar or caffeine: neither of which is healthy.

3. Remind yourself of the power of humour

Usually, a good sign that we are feeling low is that our sense of humour fades. Answer: Get it going again! Do this by watching a comic DVD, internet searching for humorous websites, watch cat videos on YouTube or read a joke book.

Sec. 4

Laughter is a good antidote to feeling low. There is plenty of evidence to show how chemicals released into the bloodstream by laughter help us to feel better.

4. Do something pleasurable for the sake of it

Everyone has their preferred way(s) of deriving personal pleasure or satisfaction. If space allowed, I could list over 1000 below! Although you might not feel up to doing it right now, you will feel the benefit of doing something pleasurable anyway.

5. Build up your physical fitness or a sufficient level of physical activity

Fit body — fit mind. Everyone can do something to improve their level of physical fitness or physical activity. It is a good daily discipline to get into.

It can range from a full marathon or a "boxer-cise" workout in the gym, to gentle arm swinging and arm and waist tensioning from a chair — and all points in between.

Again, a lot of scientific evidence is out there to prove how we can feel better when we get involved in some form of exercise, whether "high-burn" or gentle.

6. Keep self-confidence and self-esteem at a high level

Self-confidence and self-esteem are inter-connected. If we have feelings about having little personal value,

Sec. 4

our confidence is low too. Similarly, if we feel low in confidence, we will not value ourselves very much either.

The answer is to tackle either one or the other, to boost up both.

"I live in this village"

A road crash victim had been both withdrawn and isolated from others in his village for many months. He lacked the confidence to go out, having a whole collection of helpers who would bring things to him. Walking was painful due to the extent of injuries received in the crash. Also, he had a slight limp. In addition to his low self-confidence, his self-esteem was low too: he felt worthless, believing he had nothing to contribute to anyone.

With the help of a supportive friend, he was able to tell himself:

> "I have every right to walk around the village. I survived that crash in which others died and can hold my head up high; and, going for a short walk in the evening, first, will build up my confidence for a longer walk tomorrow."

> Result: Eventually he walked into the village most days, getting to know other villagers better, he was invited to play in a local skittles team, he built up his social life, spent two days a week in voluntary work and he was thinking of meeting up with a local careers advisor regarding future paid employment opportunities.

Sec. 4

7. See "the lows" as a virus which can be dealt with

"The lows" virus finds good breeding ground if both our confidence and self-esteem are low, we are feeling "stressed-out", we feel run down physically, we are pushing down our thoughts and feelings, or if we are feeling full of anger and resentment. *Anyone* can find themselves in this situation at some point in their life.

The important thing to do to defend against or defeat this virus is to work hard at all the techniques in this section. Once achieved, the results will be:

- clearer thinking,
- improved sense of humour,
- higher self-confidence and self-esteem,
- better mood,
- higher energy levels.

8. Get out there and get reconnected with supportive people

Withdrawal and isolation are common results of "the lows". Even though it may seem very hard or near-impossible, it is vital to get reconnected. Old workmates, friends from the past, relatives, friendly neighbours — in fact, anyone supportive, who you can talk to in confidence.

The principle which operates is: "A problem shared is a problem halved!" Tell yourself it is okay to talk about thoughts and feelings with people you trust, even though you might have been told some time ago that this was not permitted. Once you have done this, notice the difference made to how you feel about yourself.

9. Acknowledge to yourself that you have a touch of "the lows"

...then, take action

Often, *anything* constructive we do can get us back to feeling okay again. The domino effect applies. It does not matter what we do, giving ourselves a good talking to, taking up some physical activity, writing out thoughts, ideas and feelings on the situation, listening to inspiring music or talking to someone we trust: all can start the domino process going.

10. Increase your knowledge/get more information

Searching the internet, reading booklets or pamphlets, discussing with a friend or colleague can all help increase our knowledge about "the lows" and how to tackle them. People used to feel they were going mad or "losing it" in some way before they got to know that it is a normal, understandable situation to get in when we do not take a mentally healthy approach to things.

11. Get enough sleep

It is not quantity of sleep that is important, but *quality.* When unresolved thoughts go around and round in our minds, it is hard to get into deep sleep. It may be difficult

Sec. 4

to get off to sleep, get back to sleep on waking in the night, or waking very early. Sometimes, even though we might have slept for 9 hours, if it has not been of sufficient quality we may awaken tired and feeling exhausted.

(For many, many tips and ideas for improving sleep, see Section 5).

12. "The rainy-day letter[a]"

While some of life's difficult passages are impossible to anticipate, thankfully, they are not impossible to prepare for. That is the purpose of "the rainy-day letter". It can function as a bridge over life's chasms, not in the sense of providing numbing or "faking" the experience, but rather as a way to help transform difficult moments into experiences of mastery and hope. It is ironic that the very times when one most needs to remember strengths and resources, are often those occasions when it is easiest to forget about them. The "Rainy-Day Letter" or, if you prefer, "Rainy-Day Postcard" is a way to remind us of strengths and resources at those very times, when they are most needed.

The instructions are as follows:

How to make your own "rainy-day letter"

This is a letter from you to you. It should be written not in a moment of despair, but in a moment of relative calm and

---

[a]Yvonne Dolan, M.A. Charlie Johnson, M.S.W. Copyright 1995 Excerpted from Dolan, Y., 1998. *Beyond Survival: Living Well is the Best Revenge*. Reproduced with permission.

well-being. It is an emotional insurance policy against the inevitability of those darker moments that come at various times in life, a sort of "emergency road-side repair kit" for the spirit. The letter should contain, but is not limited to, the following:

- a list of nurturing activities to do,
- a list of nurturing people to call,
- reminders of your positive character traits,
- reminders of spiritual or philosophical beliefs that strengthen you,
- reminders of some of your dreams and hopes for the future,
- special advice or other reminders important to you.

Once completed, put your rainy-day letter in a place where you can find it easily whenever needed. Some people like to make several copies so that they can carry one in a wallet, briefcase or purse, leave one in a special drawer or car glove compartment, etc.

13. "Don't just lie there, get up!"

When we wake up in the morning and just continue lying there, the mind goes into overtime: it starts to work on the issues and concerns in our life. These issues and concerns then can seem ten times worse than when we are up and walking around.

When keeping it simple, a chemical process starts in the brain and the body, releasing bad chemicals into our system. These start flowing through our arteries, with unpleasant results.

It is important, in cases where survivors have fallen into this habit, to experiment, so as to notice the difference and benefits when getting up and getting going, rather than just lying there.

14. Breathe your way to a relaxed state

Find somewhere comfortable to sit or lie. Then, with your eyes lightly closed, empty your mind of all current thoughts. Now, after a short, slow breath in, breathe out slowly and steadily for the count of 11. Hold it for about 2 seconds. Then, breathe in again for the count of 7. Repeat this for about six or seven times. The more controlled and deliberate you are, the deeper will be your sense of relaxation. To maintain the effects for a good while after, wait for a few minutes, before slowly and carefully getting up and moving on to another activity. (This is the 7/11 diaphragmatic breathing described in earlier sections.)

15. What to do if you let "the lows" get too low

Sometimes, while going through a period of "the lows", we can let a situation spiral downwards. This is unpleasant, to say the least, as those of us who have been there can testify. Should this happen, call a "Halt!" immediately, promising yourself that you will take the first small step back — *and* within the next hour.

Should you be feeling so low that suicidal thoughts and ideas enter your mind, then there are plenty of options to take. One of these is to read through the many tools and techniques in my book (see Henden, 2017) about preventing suicidal thoughts. Another is to speak to a professional you know and can trust. Close friends or The Samaritans are options too.

Remember, suicide is a permanent solution to a short-term problem, and should be seen as such!

Section 5

Dealing with Sleep Disturbance

A. Techniques for Preparing for Bed

1. Read a book
2. Have some cereal or a milky drink
3. Watch a happy or boring film
4. Establish a routine
5. Get enough exercise
6. Eat early
7. Prepare well for bedtime
8. Open the window a little
9. Use lavender oil
10. Listen to a story

Sec. 5

11. Complete some tasks
12. Turn off the late news
13. Sort out your curtains
14. Resolve disagreements
15. Go for mattress comfort
16. Alternate quilts for the seasons
17. Go for softer pillows
18. Drink relaxing teas
19. Put your worries on hold
20. Buy some earplugs
21. Steer clear of caffeine and chocolate
22. Undress slowly for bed
23. "Larks" and "owls" help each other
24. Reduce emotional and psychological stress

B. Getting Off to Sleep

1. Lie flat and stare
2. Count sheep
3. Use "reverse psychology"
4. Turn your pillow
5. Tense and then relax your jaw
6. Count backwards
7. Read through the whole of this sub-section
8. Listen through headphones
9. Go for absolute stillness
10. Relax your shoulders
11. Worry not
12. Visualise calm scenes
13. Practise 7/11 breathing
14. Relax your jaws

Sec. 5

C. Getting Back to Sleep, if Walking or Awakened in the Night

1. Think relaxing words
2. Make a list of worrying thoughts
3. Use your favourite guided fantasy
4. Tell yourself sleep does not matter
5. Watch some TV
6. Get up and read
7. Pray for people
8. Forgive right now
9. Turn your quilt
10. Get up and do it right now
11. Crawl into a "safe and secure" tunnel
12. Use the 5-4-3-2-1 method
13. Five girls' names

It is important for us to talk through, or in some way resolve traumatic or disturbing memories and thoughts during our waking hours. If we do not do this, or we try to suppress them with drugs or alcohol, our brain will get stuck into these memories and thoughts overnight, while we are asleep. This can be the stuff of nightmares. We can be awakened by this activity and do not find it easy getting back to sleep. The main purpose of dreaming is to try and resolve the unresolved conflicts of the day. Better then, to try and resolve as many conflicts as we can during our waking hours. That is what Sections 1–4 have been about.

Prevention is better than cure. It is better if we sort out conflicts and painful memories by using the tools and

Sec. 5

techniques outlined within the above sections. However, in the following pages are some tips and techniques for:

- preparing for bed,
- getting off to sleep,
- getting back to sleep if awakened by disturbing dreams.

The following tips are addressed directly to survivors from anywhere on the spectrum of severe trauma and stress. Anyone can try them out for effectiveness — whether trauma survivors or not. When practitioners try out these tips for themselves, then they are more likely to recommend them to others.

A. Techniques for Preparing for Bed

It is helpful to create a "no-man's land" between day and night. This can be done by preparing for bedtime at least half an hour prior to getting into bed.

1. Read a book

A good way to empty our minds of all the cares and concerns of the day is to read an easygoing book, last thing at night.

2. Have some cereal or a milky drink

Many have found that a bowl of cereal or a milky drink before going to bed is helpful. This helps with digestion and diverts blood from the thinking brain.

Sec. 5

3. Watch a happy or boring film

The activity of watching a happy or boring film or DVD before going to bed puts a line under the day's cares and helps you prepare for sleep. Some television programmes can have the same effect.

4. Establish a soothing routine

Within half to one hour before going to bed, use a soothing routine that suits you best. This might involve having a soak in a hot bath, listening to your favourite music, working at a jig-saw puzzle, etc.

5. Get enough exercise

Make sure each day is well balanced with adequate mental and physical exercise. Energetic exercise at some points during the day has many benefits. Gentle exercise too, taken an hour or so after an evening meal, promotes relaxation and aids digestion. There are some mobile phone apps to help and encourage you with this.

Sec. 5

6. Eat early

Eat your evening meal at least 1.5–2 hours before bedtime. This avoids the "heaviness" which can be felt after a large meal, while trying to go off to sleep. Too much alcohol with a meal can slow down digestion and can increase that sense of heaviness.

7. Prepare well for bedtime

Avoid exciting, dynamic or focused activities during the late evening. Also avoid intense discussions or phone calls, at least two hours before bedtime.

8. Open the window a little

Opening your bedroom window slightly, to maintain a fresh air supply throughout the night can prevent "stuffiness", thereby reducing the risk of night-time waking. Also, it avoids carbon dioxide concentrations which can be as much as 70% by morning. A room temperature that is not too hot and not too cold will aid deeper sleep too.

9. Use lavender oil

Drops of lavender oil on your pillow can help you relax, prior to drifting off to sleep.

10. Listen to a story

Getting immersed in a bedtime radio story or play is a good way of preparing for sleep.

11. Complete some tasks

Think of some tasks during the day, that if you made a start or completed them, this would help you sleep that night (e.g. tax form, application form, loose shelving bracket, loose carpet, etc.).

Sec. 5

12. Turn off the late news

As television and radio news selected for listeners tends, in the main to be bad news, this can affect both sleep and dream work. You are better off listening to it earlier in the day. Listening to, as opposed to watching the news is less likely to disturb sleep too. One survivor said: "I listen to the 6 pm news, but not the 10 pm".

13. Sort out your curtains

Buy some heavier curtains, or have some existing ones lined. Make sure all gaps are covered, so as to prevent chinks of early morning light shining through. This is especially important during the summer months.

14. Resolve disagreements

It is helpful, where possible, to sort out any daytime disagreements you might have with family members or friends before going to bed. Resolved disagreements are good for settled sleep.

Sec. 5

15. Go for mattress comfort

It is helpful to ensure your bed is the most comfortable for you. Some people prefer softer mattresses than others. A good mattress is not necessarily the most expensive. It is important to pay attention to this, as we spend approximately one quarter to a third of our lives in bed. If the mattress is unsatisfactory in some way, a quick-fix/

cheaper option is to lay an old quilt or piece of foam under the bottom sheet.

16. Alternate quilts with the seasons

If using a quilt, it is important to make sure the tog rating is right for you and the season. If finances permit, alternate with summer and winter quilts, to maintain good night-time body temperature.

17. Go for softer/harder pillows

Changing your pillows for softer or harder or more comfortable ones, can be pleasant for both your face and head. Experiment with two thin pillows or one thicker one.

18. Drink relaxing teas

Have a cup of herbal tea, such as camomile, lemon verbena, lemon balm or peppermint, before going to bed. Alternatively, sipping warm water can have a similar effect.

19. Put your worries on hold

Before going to bed, write down your worries, troubles or mental conflicts in a notebook, or on a notepad, for action tomorrow, or at a definite future date. It can be more effective to put a heading on the page for the exact date and time you will give them some thought.

Sec. 5

20. Buy some earplugs

Fitting a suitable pair of earplugs can screen out all but the loudest noises that might awaken you during your time asleep. They are especially useful for light sleepers. It is important to find the right type to suit you, as some are more comfortable than others. This is important if you live near a busy road, railway or under an airport flight path. Two of the most popular types are the condensed, shaped foam, and those which are wax barrel-shaped. Many prefer to cut the latter type in half before moulding them to fit. Surprisingly (and thankfully!), while even the most effective earplugs screen out most noise, they do not seem to be effective against smoke alarms, fire alarms and alarm clocks!

21. Steer clear of caffeine and chocolate

The stimulants within strong tea and coffee, and in chocolate, are likely to delay your getting off to sleep. Keeping them out of your diet at least five hours prior to bedtime will be helpful. Some people find chillies, black pepper, mustard and strong spices eaten with food after 5 pm can cause midnight waking.

Sec. 5

22. Undress slowly for bed

Taking your time — plenty of time — to remove each item of clothing — before sliding into bed can help the body cool down better for sleeping.

23. "Larks" and "owls" help each other

If you are a "lark", and your spouse is an "owl", it is most likely you will be first to bed on nearly all occasions. If you are a "lark", a request for your "owl" to enter the bedroom and get into bed quietly when they do so, at their late hour, will reduce the risk of your being woken up. On the other hand, if you are an "owl", ask your "lark" to climb out of bed slowly and quietly, when they awake early in the morning, so as not to awaken you.

24. Reduce emotional and psychological stress

Avoid putting yourself under too much pressure. If you do so, you will find that your stress levels stay within acceptable levels and, as a result, you are more likely to sleep better. You may need to say "No" more often.

B. Getting Off to Sleep

1. Lie flat and stare

Lie flat on your back and stare at a spot on the ceiling. Try and keep your eyelids open and still, avoiding blinking, for as long as possible. Although it does not matter if you do blink from time to time, continue staring at your chosen point on the ceiling.

2. Count sheep

This is probably the most well known. It works best when you concentrate hard on the activity, taking it

Sec. 5

very seriously. Count your sheep, both on a hillside and out across the meadow and wherever else you can see them: "Two by the gate, one by the round bush, three by the stream, etc."

3. Use "reverse psychology"

Try and stay awake for as long as you can. Be as sincere and determined as possible with this. It helps if you tell yourself it does not matter if you do not sleep, you are resting anyway by lying flat. Many find they are asleep sooner, rather than later, by this method.

4. Turn your pillow

If your head is too warm, caused by too much thinking, turn the pillow over to the "cold side".

5. Tense and then relax your muscles

Beginning with your jaws, gently tense the muscles and relax them before going through the body, right down to the feet. You will feel a slight heaviness, calmness and sense of relaxation, as a result. This promotes deeper sleep.

6. Count backwards

Very slowly, count backwards in your head, in threes, from 301 down to 1.

Sec. 5

7. Read through the whole of this sub-section

If you are having difficulty sleeping, there is no better read! Choose which part you want to make use of tonight.

8. Connect your headphones

The act of listening softly to the radio or music, through headphones, creates a barrier between you and all that is "outside". As you feel sleepy, simply slide off the headphones and press the "off" switch on your radio or music system.

9. Go for absolute stillness

Lie on your back, very very still, without moving a muscle. Gently resist any temptation to move. Empty your mind of all concerns, think pleasant thoughts only. Through the stillness, sleepiness can take over.

10. Relax your shoulders

Consciously lowering your shoulders away from your earlobes can help remove the tensions of the day. First, lower the shoulders, let them return to a comfortable position, then lower them again. Let them return, before lowering them again.

Sec. 5

11. Worry not

When worries about the future come to mind, tell yourself you will deal with them in the coming weeks and days. Also, worries often revolve around things that will *never* happen.

12. Visualise calm scenes

When we visualise some of our favourite calm scenes, examining each carefully in detail, this distracts from life's cares and helps us to relax.

13. Practise 7/11 breathing

This is a powerful technique for regaining control of both our body and mind and has been featured in earlier sections. Simply breathe out for the count of 11, through your mouth, ensuring your abdomen contracts as you do so. Then, when all the breath is exhaled, allow your diaphragm to pull down, as you breathe in slowly through your nose, for the count of 7. When done correctly, *the abdomen extends and the chest remains still.* This is important and may require practice to get it right. The result will be calmness and a greater sense of being in control of both body and mind.

14. Relax your jaws

Focusing on your jaw muscles, relaxing them and allowing your mouth to hang open is a good way of reducing tension.

Sec. 5

C. Getting Back to Sleep, if Waking or Awakened in the Night

1. Think relaxing words

Say to yourself slowly and quietly, in your own mind, the following words:

"Calmness. . ."   "Sleepiness…"   "Drowsiness…"
"Relaxation…"   "Heaviness…"   "Tranquillity…"
"Serenity…"   "Peace…"   "Sweet Dreams…",
                                              etc.

Then, say them even more slowly and repeat them over again for as long as necessary.

2. Make a list of worrying thoughts

Sometimes, worries, regrets, sadness and unresolved conflicts of the day can awaken us in the form of vivid dreams or nightmares. This is a natural process, although when it happens, it is unpleasant. Without turning on the light, it is helpful to list them on a piece of paper or note-pad at your bedside, as soon as you realise what has woken you up. It is important to promise that you will act on them tomorrow, to make some progress towards resolving them or coming to terms with them in some way or other. The process of writing them down like this, seems to satisfy the brain that you have a plan for dealing with them.

Sec. 5

3. Use your favourite guided fantasy

Transport yourself to your favourite place (hillside, meadow, beach, far-off island, etc.) Call to mind five things there you can see, five things you can hear, five things you can smell, five things you can taste, and five things you can touch. Really concentrate on your favourite place, experiencing sensations such as calmness, pleasure, delight, wonder and relaxation. Stay at your favourite place for as long as you like, before drifting off to sleep. (Over 90% of people who use this method say they can never remember getting beyond half way, before sleep takes over!)

4. Tell yourself sleep does not matter

By saying to yourself, "I don't mind if I sleep, lie awake, or doze gently. I am getting valuable rest, either way". This can take the pressure off and thereby help you to get back to sleep. It is a form of "reverse psychology".

5. Watch some boring TV

Get up to go and watch some trivia or something boring on night-time TV, preferably wearing a minimum of clothing. Return to bed when either you are bored or have become too cold. The cosiness of the bed will be welcome and promote sleep.

Sec. 5

6. Get up and read

On waking in the night, get out and read an "easy-to-read" book for a chapter or few pages, before returning to bed. If you are alone in the bedroom, maybe simply sit up in bed to read.

7. Pray for people

Praying systematically for each member of your family and for your friends is purposeful and also helps distract you, as you concentrate on the needs and worries of others.

8. Forgive right now

If you are holding a grudge or some ill-feeling towards someone, forgive them totally and unconditionally right now. This is important as the only person being damaged by such feelings if you allow them to persist is you. (N.B.: Forgiving someone does not mean necessarily that you have to have any type of relationship with them.)

9. Turn your quilt

By slowly and carefully turning your quilt over to the cold side, you may cool your body down sufficiently to encourage sleep. (Best for when sleeping alone, as it could become somewhat alarming to your spouse!) Another way is to peel back the covers, temporarily, getting cool for a short while.

Sec. 5

10. Get up and do it now

If something you need to do (e.g. draft an email/letter, make a "to do" list, etc.) is going around and round in your head, if practicable, get up and do it now. Then return to bed, comforting yourself in the knowledge that it's now done and out of the way, or at least you have made a start.

11. Crawl into "a safe and secure tunnel"

Imagine you have hollowed out a small, dry, tunnel in a hillside. You have furnished it with a narrow mattress, sleeping bag and pillow. You have a small nightlight safely burning in the corner. You have carved out small shelves in the soft rock for little personal objects. Now, experience the security you feel and notice all you can see in your safe, cosy environment, before gently drifting off to sleep.

12. Use the 5-4-3-2-1 method

Open your eyes.

Notice five things that you can see.

Close your eyes.

Notice five things that you can hear.

Notice five things that you feel in your body (e.g. warmth, pillows, etc.; not emotions).

Sec. 5

Open your eyes.
Notice four things that you can see.

Close your eyes.
Notice four things that you can hear.
Notice four things that you feel in your body.

Open your eyes.
Notice three things that you can see.

Close your eyes.
Notice three things that you can hear.
Notice three things that you feel in your body.

Open your eyes.
Notice two things that you can see.

Close your eyes.
Notice two things that you can hear.
Notice two things that you feel in your body.

Open your eyes.
Notice one thing that you can see.

Close your eyes.
Notice one thing that you can hear.
Notice one thing that you feel in your body.

Repeat if necessary. (It often requires two repetitions to induce sleep.)

After using the exercise four or five times, it will become easier and the calming effect will be greater.

13. Five girls' names

"Think of five girls' names beginning with A (e.g. Andrea, Audrey, Ann, Anilese, Agatha, etc.).

Think of five girls' names beginning with B (e.g. Beryl, Bettina, Barbara, Beverley, Becky, etc.).

Think of five girls' names beginning with C (e.g. Carol, Clare, Christine, Celia and Cordelia, etc.)

Think of five girls' names beginning with D (…etc.)"

And so on . . .

(Most people do not get beyond H before drifting off to sleep.)

Sec. 5

Section 6

Living Life to the Full (or, as Full as Possible)

1. Remind yourself about your strengths, qualities, skills, resources and other personal characteristics
2. How have you used these qualities, strengths, skills, etc. up to now?
3. How will these qualities, strengths, skills, etc. be helpful to you in the future?

Sec. 6

4. Fast forwarding the DVD of your life
5. Scaling progress on the DVD of your life
6. What has been found to be helpful so far?
7. What has been found helpful in what others have said or done?
8. The power of small steps
9. Who are your main encouragers and/or supporters?
10. Write down dream(s) for the future
11. Those who have "done it", whom you most admire
12. What gives your life meaning and purpose?
13. Keeping all drugs at bay
14. Seek out intimacy of relationship
15. Reconnect with yourself
16. Reconnect to a community
17. Connect to God or "a higher power"
18. Write a letter to someone you really admire
19. Kick the "PTSD" label into touch
20. The amazing effect of the first small step
21. Do not buy in to the "depression" label
22. What helped you survive at the time of the incident?
23. What else helped?
24. What strengths and skills did you bring into play at the time?
25. What else have you been through in life that was difficult and what helped you then?
26. Which of the things that helped you then could be useful to you again now?

Sec. 6

27. Thinking of others who have gone through the same or a similar ordeal, what helped that person/those people deal with it?

28. What does it mean to you to have survived these traumatic events?

29. When these traumatic events are even less of a problem in your life, what will you be thinking about and doing instead?

30. How have the things you have experienced/happened to you made you a stronger person?

31. How have the things you experienced/happened to you made you a more determined person?

32. How do you maintain your hope that you can regain a better life in the future?

33. How will others close to you know how well you have succeeded in living life to the full?

34. What helps most to keep any intrusive thoughts and memories under control?

35. Which experiences of safety or comfort from the past do you make use of now?

36. What symbol of safety or comfort from the past do you/could you make use of now?

37. What rituals could you perform when you have reached your goal in living life to the full? How would you celebrate?

38. How do you remain hopeful and optimistic for the future?

39. If you needed more hope, how would you get that to happen?

Sec. 6

Survivors of severe trauma and stress deserve more than to know they have survived whatever incident or incidents they have experienced or were involved in (see Appendix D: Victim–Survivor–Thriver). Survival alone is not living, but is a form of existence at a lower level. "The lows" occur most within the victim stage, and they occur (though less often) in the survivor stage. Thrivers experience "the lows" far less frequently.

Living life to the full/being as fulfilled as possible, with a maximum sense of meaning and purpose must be our aim. Without meaning, purpose and direction, we are simply "as straws in the wind". "Going with the flow" (or similar) is not an option. Remember, only *dead* fish go with the flow.

Within this section, you will find some tips and techniques to help you live life to the full and thrive. Dolan (1991, 1998) outlined the three stages of survival. It is the third stage (the authentic life/living life to the full/thriver) that we need to aspire to.

It may be that we have lost a limb (or limbs), have some degree of reduced physical functioning, or have some reduced brain capacity due to traumatic brain injury. Our hearing or sight may have been affected. Whilst acknowledging fully these limitations, it is of great importance to strive to live life as fully as possible. We owe it to ourselves and those closest to us. History is peppered with stories of people who have found that their limitations were not as limiting as they first thought. There are many modern day inspiring examples too.

Sec. 6

We know from experience, that many who have been in life-threatening situations, or places of extreme danger, are thankful they survived on their return. There follows some tips, tools and techniques for opening up the discussion about living life to the full. This section has been written such that it can be used as a pull-out workbook. Most survivors approach this section with enthusiasm and commitment.

Tools and Techniques

1. Remind yourself about your strengths, qualities, skills, resources and other personal characteristics

Complete the following list:

(1)   (8)

(2)   (9)

(3)   (10)

(4)   (11)

(5)   (12)

(6)   (13)

(7)   (14)

Sec. 6

In addition, if your best friend sat opposite you, what would they add to the above:

(1)

(2)

(3)

(4)

(5)

2. How have you used these qualities, strengths, skills, etc. up to now?

Write down some examples of how or in what ways you have put some of these into practice to get to where you are today:

(a)

(b)

(c)

3. How will these qualities, strengths, skills, etc. be helpful to you in the future?

(Often a good between-session task is to do the following exercise over the next two to three weeks.)

With your same lists of answers to question 1, write down how some of these will be helpful to you as you face the challenges, decisions etc. in the future.

(a)

(b)

(c)

(d)

4. "Fast forwarding the DVD of your life"

(This technique also appears in Section 3.)

Fast forwarding the DVD is used to:

- bypass problem thinking,
- create a context for setting well-formed goals,
- encourage expectations of change,

Sec. 6

- get information about how you can make progress,
- find out about things you can do, which will get you to where you want to be.

Fast forwarding the DVD

Before asking yourself this question, it is important to bring to mind or write down the details about your current difficulties or problem situation.

Next ask yourself the following question:

"Just suppose, over there in the corner (look over at corner of the room), there is a TV and DVD player... In it, there is a DVD of my life in, say six months' time, when I have got everything sorted... In my hand there is a remote control or mobile phone (hold an actual remote control or mobile phone, etc.) I fast forward the DVD to the point where my difficulties or problem/s are sorted. I then press the "play" button on the remote. What will be the first thing I will see on the TV monitor, to let me know that my difficulty or problem/s is/are now solved?"

. . . what else will I see?   . . . what else?

. . . what will I be doing differently?   . . . what else will I be doing?

. . . what different reactions might I see in those closest to me?

. . . what else?

. . . how will my thinking have changed?   . . . how else?

Sec. 6

Answer:

Some people find the fast forwarding the DVD question easier to use than others. It involves some creative thinking to get a clear picture of something to do which is realistic, achievable, measurable and something really wanted. Work hard at this.

"I kicked into touch both the booze and the cigs"

(The same example as in Section 3.)

An ex-Serviceman, who had been deployed in four theatres of operations over a seven-year career had been medically discharged due to "alcoholism". He had received detox treatment only before leaving the service. He was referred to an NHS community mental health team for help. The worker found him living in poverty, in a small flat which was filthy. Ashtrays piled with cigarette-ends, empty wine and spirits bottles adorned most surfaces and he was in a neglected and dishevelled state.

When asked the fast-forwarding the DVD question, as above, he answered:

"I will have got control of all this drinking…"
"I will have sorted my life out…"
"I will have this place (looking around) tidied up…"

Sec. 6

What else…?:

"The smoking: I'll be down to no more than five a-day…"

"Maybe, too, I'll have spoken to those in that help office, at the Regeneration Project…"

And what else…?:

"I can't see myself working yet, but maybe I'll have a few ideas…"

"And…   I'll have sorted my head out more, so I won't need the drink to try and block it out…"   "Doesn't work for long anyway…"

5. Scaling progress on the DVD of my life

Before scaling progress, it is helpful to make the following "link statement": "I'm wondering whether a little piece of what I have just described on the TV monitor is happening already. What might that be?"

Answer:

Then:

"On a scale of 1–10, where 10 stands for everything I have described on the TV monitor happening as fully as possible, and 1 stands for it not having started, where am I right now on this 1–10 scale?"

Sec. 6

Answer (A majority of people answer 2–4½):

Q: "How come I am at this number and not ½ point lower?"

Answer:

Q: "What would I need to do to move ½ or 1 point further along, over, say, the next 2 to 3 weeks?"

Answer:

Q: "What will be good enough on this 1–10 scale for me? (Most people don't need to go for perfection, at 10)"

Answer:

Sec. 6

6. What have I done or thought about that has been found to be helpful so far?

(With any traumatic event or extreme situation in life, not only have we survived them, we have done things which have helped us. Sometimes, either we forget or downplay these useful things we have done. It is helpful to remind ourselves just what we have done — and to do so often.)

I have done/thought about and found to be helpful, at least three things. They are:

i.

ii.

iii.

Others (if applicable):

iv.

Sec. 6

v.

Also:

7. "What have I found helpful in what others have said or done?"

(With some people although they mean well, they are of little real help. Others, whether they be professionals, friends, family, etc., are found to be helpful in things they do or say.)

I can list a few here as follows:

a. Person's name:

Helpful thing done/said:

b. Person's name:

Helpful thing done/said:

c. Person's name:

Helpful thing done/said:

d. Person's name:

Helpful thing done/said:

8. The power of small steps

Sometimes we can feel overwhelmed by what lies ahead, and as a result, not do anything towards overcoming any obstacles that might be in the way. As mentioned in an earlier section, there is an old Chinese saying: "A journey of a thousand miles begins with the first small step." What is mine? Can I think of one that is an *even smaller* step, for me personally — one that I can take within the next 5–10 days?

My first small step is:

Now, complete the following:

How and when I will take this small step:

9. Who are my main encouragers and/or supporters?

It is important to bring to mind who are my main support-ers and/or encouragers. It is even more important to write down their names, telephone numbers and in what ways they encourage/support or nurture me. On low days, it is too easy to forget who they are and not ring or contact them. Writing their details below will help me stay connected.

a. Name:
    Mobile no:
    Email address:

   How they encourage/support/nurture:

b. Name:
    Mobile no:
    Email address:

    How they encourage/support/nurture:

c. Name:
    Mobile no:
    Email address:

    How they encourage/support/nurture:

d. Name:
    Mobile no:
    Email address:

    How they encourage/support/nurture:

Sec. 6

e. Name:
    Mobile no:

Email address:

How they encourage/support/nurture:

10. Write down dream(s) for the future

This can help me visualise a realistic and achievable long-term future:

What I would really like to do/achieve within the next few months/years/etc., is to:

(The importance of both visualising and writing out your dream/s for the future is that you are more likely to achieve it/them, or at least move forward a few small steps in that direction).

11. Those who have "done it", whom I most admire

Despite physical and/or psychological obstacles, many survivors of all sorts of things in life go on to live full and fulfilling lives. Reading the autobiographies of these individuals can be both encouraging and inspiring. It may be simply bringing them to mind and what they have managed to achieve and continue to achieve is helpful.

Sec. 6

Some of the more noteworthy in our current age are:

Simon Weston[a]

He is a Welsh Guardsman who received 46% burns when the Royal Fleet Auxiliary ship HMS Sir Galahad was hit by an enemy missile in San Carlos Bay during the Falklands War in 1982.

He had years of reconstructive surgery, with 70 major operations or surgical procedures.

Simon tells his story in order to motivate and encourage those like him who want to move on to the next goal, whatever it may be. His message is one of single-minded determination, not only to accept what is but also to turn that to advantage. His career demonstrates clearly how a positive mental attitude can achieve great goals.

A key saying of Simon's which has encouraged many is:

"The only obstacles to achieving one's targets and successes, are those you create for yourself."

Simon's achievements:

Sec. 6

---

[a]Weston, S. Simon Weston CBE — Official Website. www.simonweston.com (accessed 22 May 2017).

Frank Gardner[b]

He was the BBC's Security Correspondent. In June 2004, while reporting from a suburb of Riyadh, Saudi Arabia he was shot six times and seriously injured in an attack by al Qaeda sympathisers. His cameraman colleague, Simon Cumbers was shot dead in the attack. Being partly paralysed in his legs, Frank is now dependent on a wheelchair for life.

Frank's achievements:

Nick Vujicic[c]

Nicholas James Vujicic (pronounced Voo-yee-cheech) was born in Melbourne, Australia in 1982. His parents were Serbian Orthodox church immigrants from the former Yugoslavia. Having Tetra-Amelia syndrome, he was born without arms and legs. He had something that resembled a left foot at the base of his trunk, which he calls "my little chicken drumstick". Initially his mother refused to

Sec. 6

---

[b]Gardner, Frank. (2017) Frank Gardner: BBC Security Correspondent, Journalist and Author. http://www.frankgardner.co.uk/ (accessed 22 May 2017); Wikipedia. (2017) Frank Gardner (journalist). https://en.wikipedia.org/wiki/Frank_Gardner_(journalist) (accessed 22 May 2017).

[c]Vujicic, N. (2017) Life Without Limbs. www.lifewithoutlimbs.org (accessed 22 May 2017); Wikipedia. (2017) Nicholas James Vujicic. https://en.wikipedia.org/wiki/Nick_Vujicic (accessed 22 May 2017).

see her new-born son, when his condition was described to her, but later as he grew up was one of his biggest supporters and encouragers.

In childhood, he struggled with depression and loneliness, questioning the purpose of life, and even if he had a purpose at all. Often he was bullied at school but was determined to thrive. He contemplated suicide during his lowest times and at one point made an unsuccessful attempt.

Nick refuses to allow his physical condition to limit his lifestyle, and with his strong faith in God, the support of family and friends, has gone on to be a motivational speaker, musician, actor and a prolific author. His first public speaking engagement was when he was 19. He has spoken to schools, church groups and business organisations. One year he was invited to speak at the World Economic Forum in Davos.

Nick markets a motivational DVD for young people entitled: "No arms, no legs, no worries!"

He has written seven books, titles of which include:

Life Without Limits: Inspiration of a Ridiculously Good Life (2010), *Your Life Without Limits* (2012), *and The Power of Unstoppable Faith* (2014).

(For the full list, see Bibliography.)

Nick's hobbies include painting, fishing and swimming. He is married with two sons and now lives in California, USA.

Nick Vujicic is a particularly good example of how someone with profound birth handicaps can go on to live a full and productive life, being an inspiration to others

Sec. 6

who have lesser birth handicaps or disability due to life-changing injuries sustained in childhood or adult life.

Kevin Hines[d]

Kevin Hines was born to drug dealing parents and, after a chaotic early life, was taken into the foster care system. In 1986, he was adopted by Patrick and Debra Hines.

In his late teens, he developed extreme paranoia with delusions that people were out to kill him. In 1998, after a short period of mania, he was diagnosed as having a bipolar condition with psychotic features.

Such was his increasing mental pain and anguish on 24th September 2000. Kevin looked online for ways to end his life. The Golden Gate Bridge in San Francisco, his home town was recommended by one dubious website (since the Golden Gate Bridge's construction in 1937, around 2000 people have jumped to their death. Only 36, including Kevin, have survived).

While on the bus to the bridge, he was hit suddenly by the ambivalence over his decision. Looking around at the other passengers, he believed sincerely that none of them cared whether he lived or died.

In common with other survivors of suicide by jumping, a millisecond after his hands left the rail he regretted it. He wanted an end to the mental pain not to his life.

When he hit the water, he broke three spinal vertebrae. After fighting his way back up to the surface in the murky

Sec. 6

---

[d]Hines, K. (2017) The Kevin Hines Story. www.kevinhinesstory.com (accessed 22 May 2017).

waters, he cried out continuously, "God please save me!" and "I don't want to drown!". He was aware that all his depressive thoughts had disappeared. Miraculously, he was aware, too, that a sea lion had appeared and was gently supporting him from underneath. Kevin felt an overwhelming determination to survive. A coastguard speed boat rushed to his rescue and he was pulled from the water.

After a series of operations, he was transferred to the mental ill-health wing of the hospital. He came to realise that "suicide should never be the answer", and that although some mental health issues can remain, life is the most powerful single gift we have ever been given. He asserts that, "rather than his cup being half full or half empty, his cup is overflowing and exuding positivity".

Kevin Hines is a film maker, motivational speaker, author, storyteller and activist. As a survivor and now a thriver, he has devoted his life to spreading the message around the world of living mentally healthily. Kevin believes in the power of the human spirit and the fact that, despite problems we may be having, we can all find the ability to live mentally well. His mantra is: "Life is a gift, that is why they call it the present. Cherish it always."

Kevin Hines serves on various boards that champion mental health and has received many awards for his campaigning work. He is involved in policy work as an Ambassador to the US National Counsel for Behavioural Health.

Sec. 6

In sharing his story, Kevin is fostering a critical bridge of hope between life and death for people caught in the pain of living with serious mental illness, difficult life circumstances and more.

In 2006, he featured in the film, The Bridge, by producer Eric Steed, and in 2013 wrote the best-selling book, *Cracked, not broken: Surviving and Thriving After a Suicide Attempt*. There are four YouTube videos about Kevin's amazing story of survival and now his work as a thriver. In one of these, he pleads with members of the general public to be on the lookout for strangers in emotional distress, suffering and pain. He implores us to approach them — look them in the eyes — and ask: "Are you okay?", "Is there something wrong?", "Can we help?"

What people have said about Kevin Hines:

> *With an advanced degree of adversity, Kevin Hines survived the penultimate test to become uniquely qualified like no other, as an eloquent and effective witness for Wellness and Hope that an audience can ever hope to hear. He is more than a survivor; he is now a champion for anyone who needs to notch a win in the game of life.*

> Serni Solidarios, Director of Student Programmes/
> University of Puget Sound

> *I believe, with my whole heart, that Kevin's message saves lives.*

> Wende Nichols-Julien, Executive Director/
> The California Conference for Equality and Justice

Sec. 6

The entire world needs to hear Kevin's story. . . He is able instantly, to connect to individuals in crisis. . . His message is vital to any suicide prevention or resilience programme on the planet.

Commander Wayne-Boyd, US Marine Corps

I hope that you are aware of how much you have influenced my work. I tell your story quite often and even when I don't, you are more often than not, on my mind. You are saving lives, my friend, even more than you know, because you are influencing others out there who are saving lives too.

Captain Aaron Werbel PhD,
Medical Services Corps, US Navy

Kevin's website[e] gives full information about his campaigning work.

Write down here the names of others who have overcome incredible odds and are living their lives well: (They do not have to be famous)

a. Name:

Achievements:

Sec. 6

---

[e] One of the pages is devoted to merchandise, advertising tee shirts and wrist bands with slogans, #HopeHelpsHeal, #KeepOnKeepingOn and #LifeIsAGift.

b. Name:

Achievements:

c. Name:

Achievements:

12. What gives my life meaning and purpose?

"If we aim for nothing, we can be fairly certain we will hit it."

This statement is as true both for those who have had traumatic life experiences and those who have not.

For those of us who experience pain or physical limitations, it is very important to put something into our life which will give us a sense of meaning and purpose, something that will give it direction. This is the secret of good mental health and was outlined in detail over sixty years ago by a psychotherapist called Viktor Frankl (see Bibliography).

For you to gain maximum benefit from this section, it is set out in three steps as follows.

Sec. 6

"What I have done in the past that has given me a sense of meaning and purpose to my life!":

a. "What I am doing at present which gives me a sense of meaning and purpose in my life":

b. "What I will do over the next few months to a year, to give me an increased sense of meaning and purpose in my life?":

c. ...and my first small step will be:

By when:

13. Keeping all drugs at bay

Many survivors of severe trauma and stress are at risk of using drugs. It may be simply an increased use of nicotine or a heavier reliance on alcohol. It may take the form of over-the-counter drugs from the chemist and/or may be in

Sec. 6

receipt of prescribed drugs from a doctor. Nowadays, it is increasingly acknowledged that drugs for mental health issues are simply symptom-alleviation and *not* treatment. In some circumstances, these drugs may be helpful to get survivors over a short-term difficulty. For commercial reasons, generally the pharmaceutical companies that manufacture these drugs do not support short-term use. Neither are they interested in recommending withdrawal regimes, offering minimal advice only.

It is often seen as the easy option to increase drug intake as a way to soften the impact or give some relief from painful memories and experiences we would rather forget. Although this may help a little in the short term, in the long run *drugs do not work*.

Drug use — whether nicotine, alcohol, prescribed medication or street drugs — can cause other problems in both the medium and long term. This can lead to serious life-threatening illnesses and premature death (see Gøtzsche, 2013).

We owe it to ourselves to educate ourselves and others about the harmful effects of any form of drug use. There are dozens of excellent leaflets and pamphlets provided by many health promotion and wellness organisations and these should be made as widely available as possible.

There has been a lot of discussion recently about antidepressants and their effects on the brain. What we know now is that most antidepressants only work in about 30% of cases after about six months. The idea of antidepressants "correcting a chemical imbalance in the

Sec. 6

brain" has been largely debunked (Griffin and Tyrrell, 2004), and increased suicidal and homicidal tendencies and impotence, are now widely reported side-effects of several of them.

It is far better for health, if we empower ourselves and those we work with, to take control by using methods involving the natural, God-given power of our mind and body. That is what this book is all about.

Useful questions to ask are:

— How will I know when I am ready to have a conversation with my doctor about reducing my medication?
— As I begin to phase down my drug/alcohol use, what side-effects will I notice becoming less?
— When I am off all drugs, or got them down to a more satisfactory level, how will that be helpful to me?
— Once I am clear of all drugs, what will I notice about side-effects that I have no longer?

Other helpful questions to ask are:

"What have I done so far to keep drinks and all drugs at bay?"

"What will I promise myself about keeping drinks and drugs at bay over the next year?"

Breaking this down into small, realistic, and achievable steps, these are:

(1)

(2)

(3)

(4)

(5)

14. Seek out intimacy in relationships

Intimacy is a basic human need: either with a spouse, with family members, buddies or close friends. This is not about sexual intimacy, but about closeness and connectedness with those near and dear to us. Some people prefer the closeness of owning either a cat, a dog, or some other type of pet. This is okay too.

As individuals we feel more complete and fulfilled when intimacy plays an important part in our lives.

Sec. 6

Helping survivors consider ways in which this might be achieved, can be both interesting and rewarding.

Reviewing our current intimate relationships can be a useful exercise.

Questions to ask ourselves might be:

- How happy am I with my current level of intimate relationships?
- How could I become closer and more connected with them or others?

15. Reconnect with yourself

This form of reconnection can often be achieved by spending time alone, by meditating, or by making notes in a notebook or journal. It is about connecting deep within the very core of our being: with our soul/spirit.

We can review our thoughts about this and how it may have been useful to us in the past, and how it might have been working for us recently. Once we know what works/ what helps, we will benefit by doing more of it.

16. Reconnect to a community

This again is a vital human need unless we are self-declared loners or hermits.

Connection to extended family, the neighbourhood, church, a community group or an interest group, can be of great benefit. It has even greater value to us when we

Sec. 6

contribute in some way or other. We feel accepted and appreciated by others and vice versa.

"Go National"

A man in his fifties who was an adult survivor of child-hood abuse (mainly from his parents) decided to join a nationwide federation or community family trusts which promoted initiatives for strengthening marriage and the family. He helped support marriage preparation courses and parenting classes in his particular town.

17. Connect to God or "a higher power"

Most us believe we are more than simply mind and body: we have a spiritual aspect too, or there is a greater intelligence than ourselves or a being at work in life. Survivors who have a religious faith can be encouraged to develop their spiritual connectedness through prayer, religious services, meditation or study. They may seek conversion at this time. Throughout history, there have been many testimonies from people who have achieved great things through this form of connected-ness. If you do not have this belief, the massive creativity and healing power of Nature itself may appeal.

18. Write a letter to someone you really admire

This exercise is a good one for survivors who need to "aim higher" with their expectations both of themselves now and what life might have ahead for them.

Sec. 6

The instructions are as follows:

1. Think of someone you really admire. This may be someone known to you (e.g. a boss, former head teacher, an inspiring friend or relation), or someone in the public arena.
2. Imagine you are going to write a letter to them outlining all the things about them you admire.
3. Pick a quiet private half hour and actively write the letter (which of course will not be sent). Use a sheet of paper or journal for this.

The effects of writing such an imaginary letter are:

• Qualities are flagged up that you would like to have more of yourself.
• Confidence and self-esteem levels are increased.
• There is a general increase in the "feel good factor".

19. Kick the "PTSD" label into touch

Some professionals take great satisfaction from diagnosing some survivors of severe trauma and stress, affixing the label "PTSD". Labels like this, however generally are not helpful, and for some are seen as limiting at best and a life sentence at worst. Some professionals in years gone by were fond of such labels as "schizo-affective disorder", "chronic schizophrenia" and "manic-depressive psychosis". I have spent the latter part of my career helping survivors to work on their symptoms to shed

Sec. 6

these labels and to live lives which are both purposeful and meaningful. A healthier and more positive way is to rename survivors' experiences as "post-traumatic growth" (PTG) or "post-traumatic success" (PTS) (see Bannink, 2014, 2016). These are both solution-focused terms and are more positive and helpful to survivors. Diagnostic labels such as "disorder", "syndrome" and "disease" are medical terms and in the field of mental health can be debilitating and a handicap to those who embrace them fully. It is often noted that survivors "with PTSD" simply exist, survivors with PTG or PTS go on to thrive!

20. The amazing effect of the first small step

Sometimes we think about what we might like to do in the future, what we would like to achieve in life. Doubts and fears can get in the way, of us becoming the person we want to be.

The secret to making some headway in the right direction, is to think what might be the first small step. Once you have done this, think of an *even smaller* step. Then *take it!*

21. Do not buy in to the "depression" label

This is another diagnostic label most favoured by medical professionals and the pharmaceutical industry.

There are various definitions of depression and these can vary from practitioner to practitioner.

Sec. 6

Currently my two preferred definitions are those described by Griffin:

"Unexpressed emotion"; and/or

"Undeclared or unresolved issues from the past"

(Griffin, 2004)

Neuroscience now supports the view that the traditional biochemical definition of depression (that the brain has a chemical imbalance) is at best a half truth or at worst false.

Growing numbers of survivors of severe trauma can testify to the effectiveness of the tools and techniques within this book, in treating both depression and "the lows". This is achieved without the use of medication, or at most having it prescribed in the short-term only.

Finally, in conclusion, the "thriving" state not only promotes healthy lives, but also promotes longer and more productive lives. In the twenty plus years I have been teaching two-day workshops on this subject (see Appendix H) I have had the privilege of meeting many fellow thrivers who have since become therapists. Below are some of their testimonies (I have anonymised all names to protect confidentiality, although I know many would not mind):

"Coming through what I experienced, to a point now where I cannot believe how full and meaningful my life is, I just want to give back to others so they can fully live, too."

Sandra, Manchester, UK

"Although I will never forget the death and carnage I witnessed, I know now that I need not be affected by it as I was for a while following the incident. With my tried and tested techniques for triggers and unwanted thoughts, I feel equipped to deal with any reminders or memory from that terrible time. I am living my life more fully and enjoyably now than I ever did before it happened. In some way, I'm grateful to the incident for how I'm living now. Does that sound weird?"

Brian, Perth, Western Australia

"I lost my son in a tragic set of circumstances and for which I blamed myself. I felt suicidal, only in the sense I would be reunited with him in death. I went through a two-year nightmare and had to go away to a healing retreat. While there, I was taught some surprisingly helpful techniques and at the same time was encouraged to read Gerald L. Sittser's book, *A Grace Disguised: How the Soul Grows Through Loss*. He lost most of his family in a tragic car crash yet still was able to forgive and go on to live life to the full. I thought to myself: "I will, can and must do that, too". I am now a qualified therapist helping other survivors along their journey to the thriving life."

Lee Wong, Singapore

22. What helped you survive at the time of the incident?

23. What else helped?

Sec. 6

24. What strengths and skills did you bring into play at the time?

25. What else have you been through in life that was difficult and what helped you then?

26. Which of the things that helped you then could be useful to you again now?

27. Thinking of others who have gone through the same or a similar ordeal, what helped that person/those people deal with it?

28. What does it mean to you to have survived these traumatic events?

29. When these traumatic events are even less of a problem in your life, what will you be thinking about and doing instead?

30. How have the things you have experienced/ happened to you made you a stronger person?

Sec. 6

31. **How have the things you experienced/ happened to you made you a more determined person?**

32. **How do you maintain your hope that you can regain a better life in the future?**

33. **How will others close to you know how well you have succeeded in living life to the full?**

34. **What helps most to keep any intrusive thoughts and memories under control?**

35. **Which experiences of safety or comfort from the past do you make use of now?**

36. **What symbol of safety or comfort from the past do you/could you make use of now?**

37. **What rituals could you perform when you have reached your goal in living life to the full? How would you celebrate?**

Sec. 6

38. How do you remain hopeful and optimistic for the future?

39. If you needed more hope, how would you get that to happen?

Appendix A

Reassuring Things for Survivors to Know

1. Only about 15% of people who experience a traumatic incident will develop symptoms that last more than a few weeks.
2. There are both positive and negative effects from severe trauma and stress experiences.
3. If you experience symptoms, you do not have to go for therapy from a professional expert in the field. Self-help and "buddy-aid" is sufficient in many cases.

4. Getting professional help does not mean you are weak. It takes great courage to meet up, in confidence, with a complete stranger, to talk through your experiences.

5. With whatever traumatic event you have experienced, when meeting up with a professional, you do not have to go through everything or remember all that happened. Meeting a professional does not mean you are going mad and/or out of control.

6. Symptoms can be dealt with simply and effectively in the short term — without the use of medication, "depth" psychology, or long term psychotherapy (in some cases, a short course of medication may be helpful).

7. "Buying into a PTSD diagnosis", with its long-term implications, is generally unhelpful.

8. An achievable and realistic aim in recovering is a happier, more fulfilled, meaningful, peaceful and joyous life.

Appendix B

What Survivors Have Found to be Helpful in This Work

Survivors found it helpful when people:

- Enabled identification of conflicts they were experiencing/feeling.
- Encouraged working through these issues if that is what they wanted.
- Promoted self-esteem and self-confidence.
- Encouraged them to take control of their lives.

- Allowed them to choose the goals of therapy in accordance with their wishes and values.
- Maximized collaboration, minimised resistance in the work.
- Encouraged them to give up secrecy and shame in their lives.
- Gave information: both verbal and written.
- Provided a good quality therapeutic relationship for disclosing: this mobilised the person's capacity for self-healing and growth.
- Built a trusting relationship.
- Provided acceptance, and supported and encouraged them to confront conflicts where appropriate.
- Helped them to share thoughts and feelings.
- Showed understanding.
- Gave time.
- Enabled correct apportionment of blame.
- Acknowledged, validated and normalised thoughts and feelings wherever possible.
- Helped them to express emotions, thoughts and feelings.
- Simply allowed them to disclose or divulge what happened in their way and at their own pace.
- Asked what they were seeking in treatment and how they will know when their treatment has been achieved.
- Did not assume that they needed to go back and work through traumatic memories (Some do, some do not).
- On occasions, made provisions (e.g. contracts) for safety from suicide, homicide and other potentially

dangerous situations, if necessary. It was best when these were mutual.

- Remained focused on the goals of treatment, rather than getting lost in the gory details.
- Did not give the message that the person is "damaged goods" or that their future is determined by having experienced the traumatic or stressful incident.
- Admitted sometimes to getting it wrong.
- Enabled them to feel safe.

Appendix C

Helpful Questions and Statements from the Worker

From extensive and varied experience in doing this valuable work, the following questions and statements have been found to be most useful and helpful.

1. "How would you like to use these sessions?"
2. "What do you think your (friends, boss, etc.) will begin to notice about you as you sort things out in your own mind/move forward even more?"

3. "What strengths, qualities or special abilities did you call into play to survive that time/those incidents?"
4. "What have you done, up to now, not only to sort things out in your own mind, but also to be living your life well?"
5. "How much of the detail do you need to tell me before you are ready to move on?"
6. "What do you feel you need to tell me in order for me to be most helpful to you?"
7. "What particular techniques do you use to counteract any unwelcome thoughts you might be having?"
8. "On a scale of 1–10, where are you now in terms of living your life well?"
9. "What we know from this type of work is that people can work through things which might hold them back."
10. "It is quite common for people to feel guilty as a result of what happened."
11. "What has been particularly helpful to you so far in expressing your anger in safe ways?"
12. "What particular strengths, qualities, resources do you have that you have found to be helpful to you in the past, and which could be useful to you in the months and years to come?"
13. "What would be the first (smallest) sign that things are getting better, that this incident is having less of an impact on your life?"
14. "What will you be doing differently when this (incident) is less of a problem in your life?"
15. "What will you be doing differently with your time?"

16. "What useful things will you be in the habit of saying to yourself?"
17. "What will you be thinking about (doing) *instead* of the thinking about the past?"
18. "Tell me about sometimes when the above is happening to some (even small) extent already."
19. "What difference will the above healing changes make when they have been present in your life over an extended period of time (weeks, days, months, years)?"
20. "What do you think that your (significant other) would say would be the first sign that things are getting better?" "What do you think he/she will notice first?"
21. "What else have you been through that was difficult, and what helped you then?"
22. "Which of the things that helped you then could be useful to you again now?"
23. "What does having survived these traumatic events mean to you?"
24. "What difference do the changes you have accomplished, make to your family now and for future generations?"
25. "What helpful symbol of safety or comfort from the past could you use for the work you are doing here?"
26. "When you have reached the thriver stage, what ritual would you like to use to celebrate?"

(I am grateful to Fredrike Bannink for permission to include in this list some additional questions provided in her highly recommended book, *1001 Solution Focused Questions*, W W Norton & Company.)

Appendix D

The Three Stages: Victim–Survivor–Thriver (Living Life to the Full, or as Full as Possible)

Information for survivors about the characteristics of each stage:

Victim

- First stage of healing. First, it is important for you to face the reality of the bad or unfortunate thing that happened.
- You can then acknowledge the negative feelings and emotions that might be around (grief, anger, sadness, disappointment, frustration, despair, hopelessness, helplessness, etc.).
- Allow yourself to experience these feelings and emotions — and to express them.
- This is a vital part of healing plus a valuable part of this stage.
- It is also important to recognise that what happened was *not your fault*, so you can let go of self-blame and shame. In the small number of cases where it was partly your fault, it is important for you to attribute only the correct proportion of blame to yourself. Then it is important for you to consider in what ways, constructively, you may make amends for what occurred.
- Find the courage to tell someone else what happened to you; this breaks down the isolation.
- As soon as the victim stage has been acknowledged and understood, you can move into the next stage — *Survivor*.

Survivor

- This begins when you understand you have lived beyond the traumatic or highly stressful experience/s that occurred.

- This stage reinforces the fact that it happened in the past.
- Then questions may be asked: "How did I survive it?", "How did I do it?", and "What strengths and resources did I use?"
- Acknowledgment of survivorhood involves:
  — Developing an inventory of positive personality characteristics.
  — Identifying and appreciating the internal strengths (knowledge, courage, spirituality and other positive aspects of self), which have got you this far.
  — Identifying external resources (friends, support groups, telephone helplines, supportive family members, community support, etc.) at the time of the incident/s and afterwards.
- At this stage, you will regain the ability to function in everyday life: work, family time, household chores, time with friends, hobbies, community activities, etc.
- Once you have acknowledged you have survived — with skills, strengths, qualities and resources that have got you to survival and eventual wellbeing — move on to thriving/to living life to the full/living as purposeful and meaningful life as possible.

Thriver — Living Life to the Full

- This allows you more freedom than the earlier stages.
- It allows you to experience a more compelling present and to contemplate a future that is more vivid and fulfilling than your past.

- It is now possible to enjoy life to the fullest within any physical limitations you may have.
- It is worthwhile to explore possibilities and dreams for the future you may be having right now.
- It is now possible for you to express yourself in the most personally rewarding and creative ways available to you.
- In this stage, your current experiences and relationships may evoke increasingly a sense of immediacy, wonder and enhanced potential for future growth.
- You have a clear idea now about what gives you meaning and purpose in life.
- You are able to state clearly your goals for the future.
- You are living life to the full. Good feelings about both yourself and your world abound like never before.

(The above points have been developed from ideas outlined by Yvonne Dolan in her book, Beyond Survival: Living Well is the Best Revenge, BT Press 2000.)

Appendix E

Blocks to Disclosing

Below is a comprehensive list of the main "blocks" survivors have in speaking to a professional worker. With some of these, the survivor simply will not come forward at all. A large number who do will not talk much because one or several of these blocks get in the way. If you can identify the block(s), with the survivor, you may be able to help them move forward.

In some cases, survivors are able to be helped therapeutically without their disclosing what happened.

Gender of worker   Fear of rejection

Shame   Inarticulation

Not being believed	Fear of someone important finding out
Non-recognition	Lack of trust
Loss of control	Worker perceived as not understanding
Special needs disability	Reaction of worker unsure
Feeling unsafe	Betrayal of family/others
Embarrassment	Inexperience of worker
Religious beliefs	Concerns about Official Secrets
Fear of being judged	Guilt Denial

Fear of being seen as weak/soft/not able to cope

Fear of consequences	Rank/perceived status of worker

Feeling contaminated by the abuse/incident and therefore not wanting to infect/affect worker

Not wanting to be seen in a poor light by worker

Having been told by the perpetrator or others to remain silent

Previous poor experiences when disclosing

Not trusting the environment (answerphone for messages, paper-thin walls, too many windows, etc.)

Believing the worker's knowledge of the subject is insufficient

Worker lacking empathy

Appendix F

How to Avoid Retraumatisation and Revictimisation

The following eight tips have proved invaluable in helping workers do this important work both successfully, and in a helpful way for survivors.

1. Show compassion and deep empathy.
2. As the survivor discloses:

acknowledge, validate and normalise all feelings and sensations expressed.

3. Ask strength-based questions, interrupting as appropriate while the survivor is disclosing, as follows:
   - How did you cope at the time?
     — What got you through all this?
     — What most helped?
     — How did you do that?
     — How did you know how to do that?

   - Looking back on what happened, in what ways has it made you a more determined and/or stronger person?
   - Awful though it was, which aspects of surviving it have made you a better person?
4. It is important to compliment sincerely, where appropriate, both as the survivor is disclosing and most importantly at the end of the session.
5. Treat the content with care, respect and in a supportive manner.
6. Value and affirm, verbally and non-verbally.
7. Keep your own and your survivor's eyes on the treatment goals.
8. Keep to the "5 o'clock rule" (see Henden, 2017).

Appendix G

Benefits of Doing This Important Work

Whether you are a survivor or a practitioner reading this appendix, this comprehensive list, on the right-hand side, outlines the countless benefits to be gained by getting involved in this useful work. What is stopping you? What is your next small step?

No to:	Yes to:
Life of fear and anxiety	Successful personal relationships
Marital/couple break-up	Quality family life

(*Continued*)

(Continued)

No to:	Yes to:
Existence as a victim/survivor	Passing on tips and techniques to other survivors
Constant pulling around "the PTSD ball and chain"	Living life well
Excessive use of drinks, drugs or tobacco to cope	Healthy living/eating
Feeling out of control	Feeling in control; living life well
Finding difficulty resting or doing nothing in particular	Physical fitness as much as possible
Feelings of stuckness	Feelings of great joy from time to time
Fearful of unexpected triggers	Welcoming triggers to practise techniques learned
Difficulties with everyday functioning	Getting on well with day-to-day tasks
Feeling that life is meaningless and pointless	Having a sense of meaning and purpose-in-life
Disturbed sleep with recurrent nightmares	Settled sleep patterns
Feeling odd and disconnected from people	Enjoying a connectedness with people — especially loved ones
Reliving constantly what happened	Regarding what happened as being part of life, but not being dominated by it
General unhappiness and discontentedness with life	Personal goals and targets in life to look forward to
Sudden and unpredictable outbursts of anger	Safely controlled aggression
Isolating self excessively from family and friends, in particular	Having a forward view of life, in terms of chapters yet to be written

Two-Day Solution-Focused Workshops on Working with Severe Trauma and Stress

These two-day workshops have been running for over 20 years, dealing with both severe adult trauma and stress, and adult survivors of child abuse and neglect.

For enquiries, please email john@johnhendenconsultancy.co.uk

The workshop content and learning objectives are outlined below:

Workshop Content

- Welcome and Introductions
- Contracting around making it safe for people to work
- Aims and objectives
- Outline plan for the two days
- The Solution-Focused approach
- Scaling confidence
- Naming the trauma: road traffic crashes, armed robbery, sudden death, muggings, near-death experiences, natural disasters, terrorist attacks, child abuse and neglect and threats to kill
- What has been found to have worked in 1–1 work with survivors
- What survivors have found helpful
- The three stages: "victim"; "survivor"; "thriver"
- The basic tools and techniques of solution-focused brief therapy
- Survival skills outlined
- Dealing with anger and "the solution-focused feelings tank"
- Applying basic solution-focused techniques to survivors
- Sticking to "the 5 o'clock rule"
- Disclosing/divulging what happened

- The detail: how much is necessary to know?
- Blocks to disclosing
- What equips us to do this work?
- Introducing specialised techniques
- Implications of this type of work for workers and how they can look after themselves
- Getting to know the "thriver"
- The specialised techniques:

  — "Let it go...Let it go...let it go"
  — The "Stop!" technique and "replaying the video" later
  — "That was then, this is now"
  — "Dual awareness" for dealing with intrusive thoughts
  — The rainy day letter
  — Letter from the future plus how to use it
  — "Park it...and move on"
  — The solution feelings tank
  — Fast forwarding the DVD of your life
  — Write, read and shred/burn
  — "Shrinking" for dealing with flashbacks of incoming missiles
  — Dealing with "the lows"

- Purpose and meaning in life/Living life as full as possible
- How we can improve further our practice from today
- Workshop roundup/summary
- Recommended reading list
- Workshop evaluation

Learning Outcomes

At the end of the workshop, attendees will be able to:

- Demonstrate an increased understanding of severe trauma and stress, and the effects of child abuse and neglect
- Describe the characteristics of the "victimhood", "survivorhood" and "thriverhood" ("living life well"/as full as possible)
- Describe the basic solution-focused tools and techniques used with survivors
- Use a variety of specialised tools and techniques for helping survivors move further towards thriverhood/living life well/their authentic self
- Recognise how these specialised techniques can be applied to other types of potentially traumatic situations
- List the main points survivors have made about how practitioners can best be helpful
- Name the pitfalls when working with survivors of severe trauma and stress
- Highlight the most helpful and useful questions to ask
- List the key ways practitioners can look after themselves to enable them to undertake this important work
- Feel more confident in their work with a wide range of survivors

Appendix I

Supporting Research Evidence for Solution-Focused Brief Therapy

**Solution-Focused Therapy Evaluation List —
15th June, 2016 Update**

Reproduced in part with thanks and full acknowledgement to Dr Alasdair Macdonald, who hosts the full

solution-focused brief therapy (SFBT) evaluation list on his website: www.solutionsdoc.co.uk.

More than 2300 publications annually. Currently, there exist 8 meta-analyses; 6 systematic reviews; 245 relevant outcome studies including 100 randomised controlled trials showing benefit from solution-focused approaches with 69 showing benefit over existing treatments. Of 73 comparison studies, 57 favour solution-focused therapy (SFT). Effectiveness data are also available from over 8000 cases with a success rate exceeding 60%, requiring an average of 3–6.5 sessions of therapy time.

Approved by US Federal Government: www.samhsa.gov; SAMHSA — The National Registry of Evidence-based Programs and Practices (NREPP). State of Washington; State of Oregon www.oregon.gov/DHS; State of Texas is examining evidence. Minnesota, Michigan and California have organisations using SF. Finland has a Master's degree in SFT and Singapore has an approved accreditation programme. Canada has a registration body for practitioners and therapists. Sweden, Poland, Germany and Austria recognise it within their systemic practice qualification. Wales (UK) includes it in their primary mental health programme.

Many recent publications were in Farsi, Finnish, French, German, Korean and Turkish. By 2014, there were 180 publications in Mandarin (including 60 from Taiwan) as against 45 in 2009. So, this evaluation list confirms the value of the model, but is no longer sufficient in itself.

Meta-analyses (only a few studies listed here)

Carr A., Hartnett D., Brosnan E., Sharry J. (2016). Parents Plus systemic, solution-focused parent training programs: Description, review of the evidence-base, and meta-analysis. Family Process. Parents Plus (PP) programs are systemic, solution-focused, group-based interventions designed as both prevention interventions and as treatment programs for families with child-focused problems. 6–9 group session with 8–12 participants. Group session 2 hours; programs span 2–3 months. 17 studies: 919 parents engaged in PP training and 440 were in waiting list control (WLC) or treatment as usual (TAU) control groups. 6 RCT, 6 non-randomized controlled trials, 5 uncontrolled single group outcome studies. Dropout rates before post-treatment assessment ranged 2–33%. Meta-analysis of 10 controlled studies: effect size 0.58. Pooled effect sizes: child behaviour problems: PP clients better than approximately 73% of controls; goal attainment: PP clients better than 94% of controls; parental satisfaction: PP clients better than 80% of controls; parental stress: PP clients better than 70% of controls. "In most studies follow-up assessments showed that gains were maintained a number of months later." (alan.carr@ucd.ie)

Kim J. S. (2008). Examining the effectiveness of solution-focused brief therapy: A meta-analysis. Research on Social Work Practice 18:107–116. 22 studies; many factors examined. Small effects in favour of SFT; best for personal behaviour change, effect size estimate 26 (sig. $p<0.05$). Thus, SFT is equivalent to other therapies.

(Dissertation: Examining the Effectiveness of Solution-focused Brief Therapy: A Meta-Analysis Using Random Effects Modelling. University of Michigan database. Up to 6.5 sessions required. Competence in SFT requires >20 hours of training?) (johnny.kim@du.edu)

Park Jung-im (2014). Meta-analysis of the effect of the solution-focused group counseling program for elementary school students. Journal of the Korea Contents Association 14(11): 476–485. URL: http://www.dbpia.co.kr/Article/3535871. Master's theses, doctoral dissertations, and journal articles published in Korea up to May 2014 were systematically reviewed. 20 studies were eligible for the inclusion criteria. The mean effect sizes and test for homogeneity of effect size (Q-statistic) were analyzed by using Comprehensive Meta-Analysis software 2.0. Main findings: average effect sizes for Solution-Focused Group Counseling Program were ES 1.61 in self-esteem, ES 1.35 in school adjustment capacity, ES 1.07 in interpersonal relationship and ES 1.03 in self-efficacy. Moderating variables were focussed on self-esteem and sessions of one hour.

Gong H., Hsu W. S. (2015). A meta-analysis on the effectiveness of solution-focused brief therapy: evidences from mainland and Taiwan. Studies of Psychology and Behaviors (CSSCI) 13(6): 709–803. 33 studies, total 1147 participants. 33 studies from Taiwan and China: 1147 subjects. Overall effect size 0.99; school 1.01; medical settings 0.94; mainland 1.03; Taiwan 0.92. Overall 1.07 at follow-up. No correlation with year of publication.

Effective for different kinds of problems and improves client's ability to solve problems by themselves. (weisuhsu@ntnu.edu.tw) (Mandarin)

Systematic reviews (only a few studies listed here)

Bond C., Woods K., Humphrey N., Symes W., Green L. (2013). The effectiveness of solution focused brief therapy with children and families: a systematic and critical evaluation of the literature from 1990–2010. Journal of Child Psychology and Psychiatry doi: 10.1111/jcpp.12058. 38 studies included: 9 applied SFBT to internalizing child behaviour problems, 3 applied SFBT to both internalizing and externalizing child behaviour problems, 15 applied the approach to externalizing child behaviour problems and 9 evaluated the application of SFBT in relation to a range of other issues. Provides tentative support for the use of SFBT; particularly effective as an early intervention when presenting problems are not severe.

Gingerich W. J., Peterson L. T. (2013). Effectiveness of Solution-Focused Brief Therapy: A Systematic Qualitative Review of Controlled Outcome Studies. Research on Social Work Practice 23(3): 266–283. All available controlled outcome studies of SFBT: 43 studies were abstracted: 32 (74%) of the studies reported significant positive benefit from SFBT; 10 (23%) reported positive trends. The strongest evidence of effectiveness came in the treatment of depression in adults where four separate studies found SFBT to be comparable to well-established alternative treatments. Three studies examined length of treatment and all found SFBT used fewer sessions than alternative therapies. The studies reviewed provide strong evidence that SFBT is an effective treatment for a wide variety of behavioural and psychological outcomes and it may be briefer and therefore less costly than alternative approaches. (http://rsw.sagepub.com/content/early/2013/01/22/1049731512470859) DOI: 10.1177/1049731512470859

Lovelock H., Matthews R., Murphy K. (2011). Evidence-based psychological interventions in the treatment of mental disorders: a literature review. Australian Psychological Association http://www.psychology.org.au/Assets/Files/Evidence-Based-Psychological-Interventions.pdf. SFBT shows Level II effectiveness for depression, anxiety and substance misuse.

Published follow-up studies (245):
Randomised controlled studies (100)
(only a few studies listed here)

Ahramian A., Ahmadi A., Shamseddinilory S., Yousefi S., Abdolahi S., Soudani M., Ghazi G. (2014). The effectiveness of group training of solution-focused approach on marriage adjustment of couples that call on Bushehr family counseling centers. (Iran) Terapevticheskii Arkhiv 86(1s). Couples; randomised; 22 exp sf groups/22 controls. Exp significant improvement in marital adjustment. (Persian)

Baldry E., Bratel J., Dunsire M., Durrant M. (2005). Keeping Children with a Disability Safely in their Families. Practice: Social Work in Action 17(3):143–156. DOI:10.1080/09503150500285099 55 care-givers from 40 families in crisis; family-centred intervention programmes (Australia). Objective measures: empowerment, emotional support, parent–child involvement, abuse potential, family functioning, symptom reduction, hope, happiness and worker–client alliance; also qualitative interviews. Significant improvement in abuse potential and emotional support at 6 mon and 12 mon ($p<0.001$). Symptom reduction and emotional support predicted 86% of variance at 12 mon. Helpful: wholly attentive listening, support, increased parent control/empowerment, validation and maintaining a strengths focus; programmes being family-focused, having 24 hours/phone availability, being home-based, with small case-loads, financial support and a consistency of worker. (e.baldry@unsw.edu.au)

Bagajan K. Q., Khanahmadi O., Chaharborj Z. M., Chenaparchi M. (2016). The Impact of Solution-Focused Brief Therapy on the Improvement of the Psychological Wellbeing of Family Supervisor Women. International Journal of Social, Behavioral, Educational, Economic, Business and Industrial Engineering 10 (1). Random: 15 exp 5 sf sess/15 controls no treatment. Significant increase in wellbeing for exp at post-test. (kawe.ghaderi@gmail.com) (Persian)

Grant A. M. (2012). Making Positive Change: A Randomized Study Comparing Solution-Focused vs.

Problem-Focused Coaching Questions. J Systemic Therapies 31(2): 21–35. Random: real problem and set a goal. Measures: positive and negative affect, self-efficacy, goal attainment. 108 participants: problem-focused coaching questions; 117 participants: solution-focused questions including future-oriented question; then second set of measures. Both effective in enhancing goal approach; solution-focused group significantly greater increases in goal approach, positive affect, decreased negative affect, and increased self-efficacy; and generated significantly more action steps to help them reach their goal. Although real-life coaching conversations are not solely solution-focused or solely problem-focused, agents of change should aim for a solution-focused theme.

Hsu W. S., Chen Y. F., Sun S. T. M., Wu C. Y., Cheng H. C. (2009). A study of working alliance, counselor's effectiveness, and client's satisfaction of solution-focused real-time webcounseling on Taiwanese college students. Bulletin of Southern Taiwan University 34 (2), 57–70. Real-time web counselling designed by Information Management of National Chi Nan University, Taiwan. 3 counsellors trained. Randomised: 8 students sf; 10 students non-sf; 1–6 weekly sess. Pre-post measures: better scores for alliance and effectiveness after 1st session for sf. Exp group significantly higher scores for counsellor effectiveness and client satisfaction, not alliance. (weisuhsu@ntnu.edu.tw)

Lindforss L., Magnusson D. (1997). Solution-focused therapy in prison. Contemporary Family Therapy

19:89–104. 2 randomised studies: (1) Pilot study 14/21 (66%) exp. and 19/21(90%) controls reoffended at 20 mon. (2) 30 exp; 29 controls; 16 mon follow-up. 18 (60%) reoffend in exp., 25 (86%) in control; more drug offences and more total offences in controls. Avg 5 sess; 2.7 million Swedish crowns saved by reduced reoffending. (lindforss@ chello.se; dan.magnusson@brottsforebygganderadet.se)

Ma Jianmin (2015). Focus-solving model used in patients with chronic health. Education Management Journal of Clinical Nursing 4. Doi: 10.3969/j.issn.1671-8933.2015.04.017 Chronic hepatitis B; random: 50 exp sf health education/50 controls routine education. Knowledge significantly increased post-test; liver function improved. (Mandarin)

Sun Yunxia, Wu Lin, Guo Xiangrong (2015). Application effects of solution focused approach on psychological nursing in patients with MRI examination Chinese Journal of Modern Nursing 26. MRI subjects with claustrophobia; random; 64 exp 5 sess sf counseling/64 TAU. Patients and caregivers report less anxiety/depression/dyspnea 26.5% exp vs 37.5%/sweating 46.8% vs 64.1%: p <0.05. doi: 10.3760/cma.j.issn.1674-2907.2015.26.005 (Mandarin)

Theeboom T., Beersma B., Van Vianen A. E. M. (2015). The differential effects of solution-focused and problem-focused coaching questions on the affect, attentional control and cognitive flexibility of undergraduate students experiencing study-related stress. Journal of Positive Psychology, DOI: 10.1080/17439760.2015.111712661. Random 31 exp sf questions about preferred future/30 controls problem-focused questions; higher positive affect, lower negative affect in exp; no effect on attentional control. Repeat 28 exp/26 controls: same results for affect. More cognitive flexibility in exp; apparently not mediated by positive affect. (t.theeboom@uva.nl)

Wang Shan, Xu Jin-zhi, Zhang Jin-feng (2015). Effects of solution-focused approach in the rehabilitation training of patients with lung cancer. Chinese Journal of General Practice 13(10). Random: 40 exp rehab exercises; sft/40 controls rehab exercises. Quality of life and health status significantly better ($p < 0.05$) in exp at 3 mon. (Mandarin)

Zhou Li-li, Ji Tian-rong, Liu Feng, Bu Zhi-hua, Liu Li, Yang Xiao-yun (2013). Effect of nursing intervention based on solution-focused approach on self-management ability of patients with maintenance hemodialysis. Chinese Journal of Modern Nursing 34. Randomised: 60 exp (SF nursing)/60 controls (routine nursing). 6 mon follow-up: knowledge of disease and self-management significantly improved in exp group. Doi:10.3760/cma.j. issn.1674-2907.2013.34.004 (Mandarin)

Comparison studies (73) (only a few studies listed here)

Amiri H., Sharme M. S., Zarchi A. K., Bahari F., Binesh A. (2013). Effectiveness of Solution-Focused Communication Training (SFCT) in Nurses' Communication Skills. Iranian Journal of Military Medicine 14 (4): 279–286. 71 nurses from medical-surgical departments of Tehran hospital. 8-hour workshop; pre-test; post-test two months after.

3 questionnaires completed (participant, head nurse, colleagues). Mean difference statistically significant [$p = 0/001$]; also between mean scores of 4 subscales of nurses' communication skills. (amirizh@yahoo.com)

Antle B. F., Barbee A. P., Christensen D. N., Martin M. H. (2008). Solution-based casework in child welfare: preliminary evaluation research. Journal of Public Health Child Welfare 2(2): 197–227. Study 1: fully trained workers, 27 cases; minimal trained, 21 cases. Better compliance, less legal action, fewer removals in trained group. Study 2: 51 cases from fully trained, 49 minimal. Better compliance and goal achievement in both urban and rural areas.

Connell M. A. (2014). Modifying Academic Performance Using Online Grade Book Review During Solution-Focused Brief Therapy. Walden University Dissertation 3631272. Three groups of at-risk students: Group 1 SFBT only (18); Group 2 (20) SFBT and Online Grade Book Review (JumpRope); Group 3 (22) JumpRope alone. Results suggested statistical significance of including gradebook review within SFBT resulted in improved academic performance.

Corcoran J. A. (2006). A comparison group study of solution-focused therapy versus "treatment-as-usual" for behavior problems in children. Journal of Social Service Research 33:69–81. 239 children; 83 sft vs 156 'treatment as usual'. Better treatment engagement with sft but no outcome differences. (jcorcoran@vcu.edu)

Franklin C., Moore K., Hopson L. (2008). Effectiveness of Solution-Focused Brief Therapy in a School Setting.

Children and Schools 30(1):15–26. 30 exp (School A); 5–7 groups; 29 control (School B); 1 mon follow-up (43). Teachers: externalised and internalised behaviours significantly improved, students externalised behaviours significantly improved.

Stith S. M., Rosen K. H., McCollum E. E., Thomsen C. J. (2004). Treating intimate partner violence within intact couple relationships: outcomes of multi-couple versus individual couple therapy. Journal of Marital and Family Therapy 30:305–318. 14/20 individual couples, 16/22 multi-group couples completed program, 9 couples comparison group; all mild-to-moderate violence. Follow-up (females contacted): 6 mon recidivism 43% individual, 25% multi-group, 67% comparison; 2 yr recidivism: 0%, 13% (one client), 50%. (Additional cases reported McCollum E. E., Stith S. M., Thomsen C. J. (2011). Solution-focused brief therapy in the conjoint couples treatment of intimate partner violence. Reduced physical aggression in both sexes for 17/20 individual couples; reduced in males only for 27/29 multi-group couples. In Franklin C., Trepper T., Gingerich W. J., McCollum E. (eds). Solution-focused Brief Therapy: A Handbook of Evidence-Based Practice. Oxford University Press: New York 2011.) (sstith@vt.edu)

Naturalistic studies (72) (only a few studies listed here)

Archuleta K. L., Burr E. A., Bell Carlson M., Ingram J., Irwin Kruger L., Grable J., Ford M. (2015). Solution Focused Financial Therapy: A Brief Report of a Pilot

Study. Journal of Financial Therapy 6(1):2. http://dx.doi. org/10.4148/1944-9771.1081. Pilot study: solution-focused financial therapy client intervention approach. 8 college students: variety of financial issues related to budgeting, investing and debt repayment problems. 3 mon follow-up: psychological well-being and financial behaviors improved, financial distress decreased.

Beyebach M., Rodriguez Sanchez M. S., Arribas de Miguel J., Herrero de Vega M., Hernandez C., Rodriguez Morejon, A. (2000). Outcome of solution-focused therapy at a university family therapy center. Journal of Systemic Therapies 19:116–128. 83 cases; telephone follow-up, most 1 yr +. 82% satisfied; better outcome for 'individual' problems than for 'relational'; more dropout for trainees; avg. 4.7 sessions (mark.beyebach@upsa.es)

Dumciene A., Rakauskiene V. (2014). Encouragement of Physical Activity among Students by Employing Short-term Educational Counselling. Procedia-Social and Behavioral Sciences 116:1523–152. http://dx.doi. org/10.1016/j.sbspro.2014.01.428 92 students; after sf counselling, 44.6% previously facing physical activity issues achieved prominent changes, 21.7% achieved medium changes and 33.7% showed minor changes. Physical activity increased, $p < 0.05$.

Fadilah N., Setiawati D. (2015). Application solution brief focused therapy (sfbt) to improve disclosure of self in Class VIII SMPN 1 Prambon. Journal BK UNESA 5(3). 5 junior high school; low self-disclosure; improved significantly post-test after sf counseling. (nurfadillah994@ymail.com) (Indonesian)

Macdonald A. J. (2005). Brief therapy in adult psychiatry: results from 15 years of practice. Journal of Family Therapy 27:65–75. Further 41 cases reported; 1 yr follow-up. 31 (76%) improved; avg. 5.02 sessions; 20% single sessions. Combined total 118; 83 (70%) improved; avg. 4.03 sessions; 25% single sess. Fewer new problems in good outcome group. Longstanding problems predict less improvement; equal outcome for all social classes.

Shennan G., Iveson C. (2011). From Solution to Description: Practice and Research in Tandem. In Franklin C., Trepper T., Gingerich W. J., McCollum E. (eds). Solution-focused Brief Therapy: A Handbook of Evidence-Based Practice. Oxford University Press: New York 2011. 4 studies. 24 clients, 6 mon-1 yr follow-up: 23 (83%) better, 1 (3%) worse. 39 clients, avg. 18 mon follow-up: 31 (80%) better, 2 (5%) worse. 57 clients 2–3 yr follow-up: 24 (59.7%) improved, 2 (3.5%) worse. 25 clients, 8 mon-16 mon follow-up: 'best hopes' achieved by 14 (56%), little 7 (28%), not at all 4 (16%).

Wiseman S. (2003). Brief intervention: reducing the repetition of deliberate self-harm. Nursing Times 99: 34–36. First self-harm 40 clients; 1 session. Up to 6 mon follow-up: 39 (97%) no repeat; 78% improved on self-scaling.

Yang Jee-Won, Kim Hyung-Mo (2015). A Research on the Effects of Solution-focused Group Art (2015) A Research on the Effects of Solution-focused Group Art Therapy on Improvement of Sibling Relationship and Well-being. South Korea Art Psychotherapy Association

Article XIV:29.11(1):147–176. www.earticle.net/article. aspx?sn=244197. 6 siblings: 10 sessions Group Art therapy. Positive effects on sibling relationship, Gentleness, Conflict, Relative status, Competition and the well-being of sibling children. (Korean)

Other resources (only a few studies listed here)

Franklin C., Trepper T. S., Gingerich W. J., McCollum E. (eds). Solution-focused Brief Therapy: A Handbook of Evidence-Based Practice. Oxford University Press: New York 2011.

Bibliography

Bannink, F. (2014). *Post Traumatic Success*: *Positive Psychology & Solution-Focused strategies to help clients survive and thrive.* New York: Norton.

Bannink, F. (2016). *1001 Solution-Focused Questions.* New York: Norton.

Dolan, Y. (1991). *Resolving Sexual Abuse: Solution Focused Therapy & Ericksonian Hypnosis for Adult Survivors.* New York: Norton.

Dolan, Y. (1998). *Beyond Survival: Living Well is the Best Revenge.* London: BT Press.

Dolan, Y. and Johnson, C. (1995). In Dolan, Y. (1998), *Beyond Survival: Living Well is the Best Revenge.* London: BT Press.

DSM-V. (2013). *The Diagnostic and Statistical Manual of Mental Disorders, Fifth Edition.* Wahington: American Psychiatric Association. Rothschild, B. (2000), *The Body Remembers: The Psychophysiology of Trauma and Trauma Treatment. New York:* Norton.

Erickson, M. H. In Haley, J. (1973), *Uncommon Therapy: The Psychiatric Techniques of Milton H. Erickson.* First Edition. New York: Norton.

Gardner, Frank. (2017). Frank Gardner: BBC Security Correspondent, Journalist and Author. http://www.frankgardner.co.uk/ (accessed 22 May 2017).

Frankl, V. E. (1959). *From Death-Camp to Existentialism:* Boston: Beacon Press.

Frankl, V. E. (1960). *Paradoxical Intention: A Logotherapeutic Approach. American Journal of Psychotherapy,* **14**, 520–535.

Frankl, V. E. (1963). Experience with the Logotherapeutic Technique of Paradoxical Intention in the Treatment of Phobic and Obsessive-Compulsive Patients. (Paper read at the *Symposium of Logotherapy at the 6th International Congress of Psychotherapy*, London, UK, August 1964) *American Journal of Psychiatry*, **CXX 111**, No. 5 (1966), 548–553.

Frankl, V. E. (1964). *Man's Search for Meaning: An Introduction to Logotherapy.* London: Hodder & Stoughton.

Frankl, V. E. (1973). *The Doctor and the Soul: From Psychotherapy to Logotherapy.* Harmondsworth: Pelican Books.

Frankl, V. E. (1976). *Psychotherapy & Existentialism: Selected Papers on Logotherapy.* Harmondsworth: Pelican Books.

Frankl, V. E. (1978). *The Unheard Cry for Meaning.* London: Hodder & Stoughton.

Gøtzsche, P. C. (2013). *How Big Pharma and Organized Crime has Corrupted Healthcare.* London: Radcliffe.

Griffin, J. and Tyrrell, I. (2004). *Human Givens: A New Approach to Emotional Health and Clear Thinking.* Delhi: H. G. Publishing.

Henden, J. (2011). *Beating Combat Stress: 101 Techniques for Recovery.* Hoboken, NJ: Wiley-Blackwell.

Henden, J. (2017). *Preventing Suicide: The Solution Focused Approach.* Second Edition. Hoboken, NJ: Wiley-Blackwell.

Hines, K. (2013). *Cracked, not Broken: Surviving and Thriving.* Lanham: Rowman & Littlefield Publishers.

Hines, K. (2014). The Kevin Hines Story. https://www.youtube.com/watch?v=loiGNZTfu6g (accessed 22 May 2017).

Hines, K. (2015). I Jumped off The Golden Gate Bridge. https://www.youtube.com/watch?v=WcSUs9iZv-g (accessed 22 May 2017).

Hines, K. (2017). The Kevin Hines Story. www.kevinhinesstory.com (accessed 22 May 2017).

Jacob, F. (2001). *Solution Focused Recovery from Eating Distress.* London: BT Press.

Sittser, J. L. (2009). *A Grace Disguised: How the Soul Grows Through Loss.* Grand Rapids: Zondervan.

Studio 10. (2017). Suicide Survivor Kevin Hines. https://www.youtube.com/watch?v=2XY96V13QbM (accessed 22 May 2017).

Vujicic, N. (2012). No Arms, No Legs, No Problem. Promotional DVD for young people. www.youtube.com/watch?v=JpnMNzQKXaQQ (accessed 22 May 2017).

Vujicic, N. (2010). *Life without Limits: Inspiration of a Ridiculously Good Life.* New York: Crown Publishing Group.

Vujicic, N. (2012). *Your Life without Limits.* New York: Crown Publishing Group.

Vujicic, N. (2010). *Life without Limits: Inspiration for a Ridiculously Good Life.* New York: Crown Publishing Group.

Vujicic, N. (2013). *Unstoppable: The Incredible Power of Faith in Action.* New York: Crown Publishing Group.

Vujicic, N. (2013). *Limitless: Devotions for a Ridiculously Good Life.* New York: Crown Publishing Group.

Vujicic, N. (2014). *The Power of Unstoppable Faith.* New York: Crown Publishing Group.

Vujicic, N. (2015). *Stand Strong: You can Overcome Bullying (and Other Stuff that Keeps You Down).* New York: Crown Publishing Group.

Vujicic, N. (2016). *Love Without Limits. A Remarkable Story of True Love Conquering All.* New York: Crown Publishing Group.

Vujicic, N. (2017). Life Without Limbs. www.lifewithout-limbs.org (accessed 22 May 2017).

Weston, S. Simon Weston CBE — Official Website. www.simonweston.com (accessed 22 May 2017).

Wikipedia. (2017). Nicholas James Vujicic. https://en.wikipedia.org/wiki/Nick_Vujicic (accessed 22 May 2017).

Wikipedia. (2017). Frank Gardner (journalist). https://en.wikipedia.org/wiki/Frank_Gardner_(journalist) (accessed 22 May 2017).

Wisegeek. What is the Diaphragm Muscle? www.wisegeek.com/what-is-the-diaphragm-muscle.htm (accessed 22 May 2017).

Index

Printed in Great Britain
by Amazon

12405728R00120